# THREE MILLION WHEELBARROWS

# THREE MILLION WHEELBARROWS

## THE STORY OF THE EAU BRINK CUT

### KATHLEEN SAUNDERS

# Three Million Wheelbarrows

## The story of the Eau Brink Cut

First published in 2021
by Mousehold Press
6, Constitution Opening
Norwich, NR3 4BD

www.mousehold-press.co.uk

Maps by Terence Loan

ISBN  978-1-874739-92-0

Printed by Page Bros, Norwich

# Contents

Front cover: View of the opening of the Eaubrink Cut, 1821
(Artist unknown)

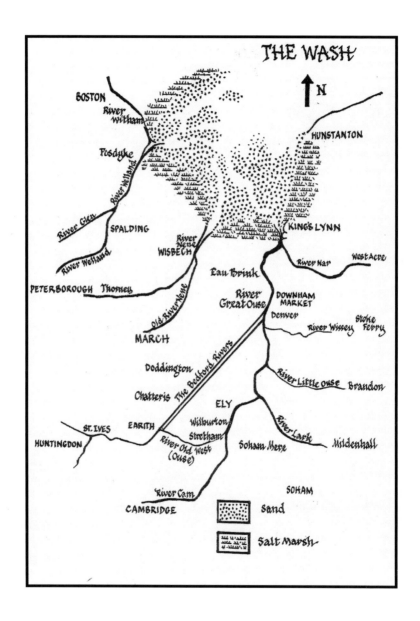

THE WASH

N

BOSTON
River Witham
Fosdyke
River Welland
River Glen
SPALDING
River Welland
PETERBOROUGH   Thorney
Old Riverbene
MARCH
Doddington
Chatteris   The Bedford Rivers
ST. IVES   EARITH
HUNTINGDON
River Old West (Ouse)
River Cam
CAMBRIDGE

River Nene
WISBECH
Eau Brink
River Great Ouse

HUNSTANTON

KING'S LYNN
River Nar   West Acre
DOWNHAM MARKET
Denver   River Wissey   Stoke Ferry
River Little Ouse   Brandon
ELY
Wilburton
Stretham
Soham Mere   River Lark   Mildenhall

SOHAM

Sand

Salt Marsh

vi

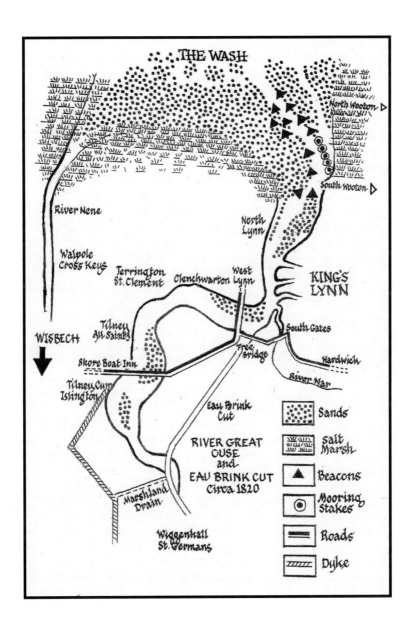

THE WASH

North Wooton

South Wooton

River Nene

North Lynn

KING'S LYNN

Walpole Cross Keys

Terrington St. Clement

Clenchwarton

West Lynn

WISBECH

Tilney All Saints

South Gates

Hardwick

Shore Boat Inn

Free Bridge

River Nar

Tilney Cum Islington

Eau Brink Cut

RIVER GREAT OUSE and EAU BRINK CUT Circa 1820

Marshland Drain

Wiggenhall St. Germans

Sands

Salt Marsh

Beacons

Mooring Stakes

Roads

Dyke

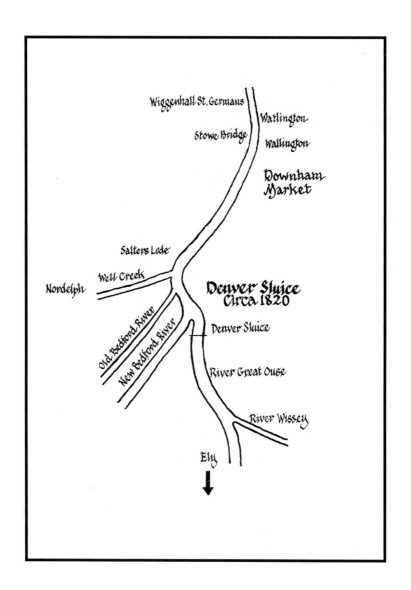

# Acknowledgements

This account of the River Great Ouse was sparked initially by the river itself and its near hypnotic effect on many who watch it flow through our towns and villages. Then, by the fascinating lives of some of the people who have tried to manage its troublesome waters. I would like to thank all those who made documents available to me, in particular Luke Shackell of the Kings Lynn Borough Archives and his colleagues at the Norfolk Record Office, and Sue Sampson of the Cambridgeshire Archives Service. Abby Pettifar and her colleagues of the Norfolk Library Service at Gaywood sourced my obscure requests with exceptional efficiency and cheerfulness.

A huge thank you goes to the multitude of informal local and family historians whose studies have been explored extensively. Those who have made their findings available on websites are particularly appreciated. My thanks also to the many who are involved in digitising older texts or making databases and catalogues available online, whose work has enriched the telling of this story. Any errors are entirely mine.

Writer friends who generously shared their skills have been my inspiration. They include Sue, Caroline, Carol, Pen, Claire, Chris, Tim, Alex and Kevin. Your company on this journey has been a delight.

Thank you always to my family, whose patience with my obsession over more years than I care to admit has been my encouragement and joy.

# Prologue

*I am and will be. I flow from the hills and run over the land, curving ever wider and deeper. When rains come I rise, more powerful than the land itself. I meander where I please and dance with the tide as I reach the ocean.*

*Men come. I let them stray in the margins of my kingdom. They float on me, trap my silken eels and tread my shoulders with their earth creatures. They wrinkle and fall. They pass in an instant and their bones enrich my soil.*

*When they stack barriers in my way I go elsewhere. My stout fingers swell and I spread my shimmering crinoline across their golden fields. They drive wooden blocks into my sides and stand on me, and I endure them, for a while. They pile stones and span bridges over me, but I overcome them.*

*I shave their supports, tide by tide.*

*I expel them like splinters.*

*The earth mends my scars.*

*Their ships come from the sea and dig claws into me at their landings. I drop sand and silt, somewhere, anywhere, and unsuspecting, they bury their hulls in my softness. They wait for the tide to spring, for sails to fill, but when my winds are strong they jostle and shatter.*

*They spill their loads into my depths, and I consume them.*

*If I look well on them I give them deep channels till they reach their docks. Men shake hands and turn their backs on me.*

*But if they sting with their bitterness, I call on the waves to come and the wind to blow. I destroy them.*

# Part One
# The Glistening

# Part One
# The Glistening

**Ely, Cambridgeshire**
**Autumn 1774**

*I watch the rich landowners hold on tight as their carriages bump their way to Ely. They gather in crowds to demand that I must be controlled. I must be made thinner and deeper to flow to the sea more quickly.*

*They want to drain the peatlands and marshes, to make them green and turn them to gold. They don't heed concerns that barges will struggle to navigate on fast waters.*

*Ships that bring timber from distant lands and colliers with their black stones need shelter in a deep harbour. My bargemen know I will drop silt and sand if my tides are slowed by narrow channels. They fear the harbour will become too shallow for large vessels.*

*The shipmasters, merchants and townspeople of King's Lynn argue, as they have always argued, with the aristocracy, financiers and landowners of the Bedford Level Corporation.*

'Enough! Something must be done!' the landowners complain. 'The River Great Ouse floods our lands every winter. We are ruined.'

'Clear your drains,' the merchants shout back. 'Tear down Denver Sluice! Remove that obstruction to the river's flow and the silt and sands will wash back out to sea. Your land will be restored.'

'Never! Denver Sluice is a barrier that protects upstream

lands from the tides and keeps water in the river for your vessels!'

'Denver Sluice does not work! The force of the tides keeps the gates shut so fresh water from high ground can't drain out to sea. It backs up and bursts your banks. Our barges are grounded for lack of water while your fields nearby are flooded,' the bargemen reply as one.

'Repair the banks and take down Denver Sluice. Only then will there be enough power in the river to scour the sandbanks back to sea,' say the merchants.

'The river's power is lost in the curve above Lynn. It must be straightened,' the landowners resolve.

'A straight, narrow river will create such violent currents that the harbour will be destroyed,' the merchants insist. 'We know how this river behaves, we use it every day. There will be no safe haven for ships. There will be no barge passage for your crops. You will get no supplies,' they predict.

There is no common ground. Men with a more diplomatic turn of mind speak up.

'We can commission engineers to design a scheme to take account of all interests.'

'And who will pay for their grand design?' the answer snaps back.

'Are we to pay more taxes to the Bedford Level Corporation? We pay too much already for their deluded schemes.'

'Remove Denver Sluice!' a chant begins. 'Restore the old currents and these problems will be solved.'

'That'd be cheaper,' reason some, but more yell above them.

'No to more plans! Clear the drains, mend the banks and there'd be no need for fancy plans with unpredictable effects.'

The merchants will not compromise.

The Chairman loses patience. He calls for a show of hands for engaging the best engineers in the country to give their opinion.

And there being fewer hands against it, the landowners gallop to a majority.

## The River Great Ouse
## 1775

> *I lead the red men, a cluster of early poppies bending against the March wind. They follow Lieutenant Hyde Page who is a military engineer, like his father before him. He sits upright on his horse, a tidy, lithe figure at the peak of manhood. His gentleman servant follows, discreetly ensuring his master remains accustomed to fine living. Hyde Page turns out each day with well brushed lapels on his scarlet coat and yesterday's mud splashes beaten from his pale breeches. Always, his boots shine. The cadets gaggle together, seeking assurance from each other. They are keen to impress but ignorant of my ways.*

The Lieutenant comes at the asking of Lord Townshend of Raynham Hall, owner of one of the largest estates in Norfolk. He is the mightily powerful Master-General of Ordnance, in charge of supplying the country's defence forces with every need. From its head-quarters at Woolwich Arsenal, military engineers and surveyors are sent to build harbours, forts and all manner of essentials for defence and exploration.

Lord Townshend is also a Bailiff, or senior member, of the Bedford Level Corporation, which is responsible for draining waters from the Fenlands. As such he is a Commissioner of Sewers, with legal authority over rivers, sewers, drains, bridges and sea defences. Many of his neighbours have had land ruined by flood, but criticism of the Corporation annoys him. The Corporation has always been underfunded.

Lord Townshend finds himself a principal director of operations since John Russell, Duke of Bedford died, leaving his ten year old grandson, Francis, as nominal Governor of the Bedford Level Corporation. In anticipation of this, the ageing Duke ensured succession passed to his widow and elder daughter, who are represented on the Corporation's Board by their lawyer, Robert Palmer, who was brought in as a Bailiff.

The five other Bailiffs vary in their experience. They are immensely wealthy men, commonly lawyers and Ministers of Parliament. One, Soame Jenyns, of Bottisham, MP for Cambridge, is a descendant of the Jenyns family who have been the backbone of the activities of the Bedford Level Company since its creation over a century before. Of them all, it is he who has the Bedford Level in his blood.

The Board is completed by twenty Conservators, whose Bedford Level estates are too small for them to be eligible as Bailiffs. They have seen severe floods come and soak away but mainly, the Corporation relies for its expertise on numerous surveyors and engineers whose varying opinions render the Bedford Level Corporation impotent and deeply indebted.

Lord Townshend knows Hyde Page will assess the situation according to successful military principles, with none of the bluster he hears from self-promoting experts. Hyde Page will recommend an effective remedy to contain floods and keep navigation moving. Better still, it won't cost the impecunious Bedford Level Corporation a single half-penny.

With this survey as an excuse, Hyde Page can also visit Thomas Pownall who is the recently returned Governor of Massachusetts in the American colonies and now a Minister of Parliament. Pownall's family own farmland at Saltfleetby, alongside the Lincolnshire coast. They know well enough what works are needed to protect crops and livestock against flooding and it would be useful to have him on their side in Parliament. He says he's found an effective way to prevent erosion using rush mat faggots staked to the banks along his estate which boarders the River Great Ouse at North Lynn. Hyde Page doesn't need telling about fascines, as these mats are known to engineers, but he could gain useful intelligence on the territory around the major colonial port town of Boston, Massachusetts.

Hyde Page will have to be stealthy. Pownall calls himself a loyalist, but some think he's turned in his sympathies. From America and since he's returned, he's done all he can to convince Parliament that the colonials should have the same rights as the British because they serve under the same King. Pownall says we should be united as one, and they should be treated as if they live in a distant county of Britain. He suggests that the revolutionaries would pay their taxes willingly if they were granted representation in Parliament. He is misguided, for they have even refused to fund their own defence against the French, who will pounce from the northern Americas into British lands given half a chance.

Lord Townshend reflects that he didn't risk his own life to conquer the French at Quebec and receive their surrender when General Wolfe was killed, only to hand the colony to these varmints now. His own brother Charles, as Chancellor of the Exchequer, devised new taxes to fund defence but the colonials rejected them all.

King George has decided these rebels must be dealt with and at this very moment, Townshend is preparing ships to embark troops for Boston. Hyde Page will be called to sail with General Howe any day now, but this Bedford Level work will keep him usefully occupied in the meantime.


### Earith, Cambridgeshire
### March 1775

*I see Hyde Page set out east from Earith, Cambridgeshire, to inspect my ancient path. Rain from upland counties that once strengthened my course to sea is now split from me, and runs in the two channels of the Old Bedford and One Hundred Foot Rivers, which bend away to the north with the land between them allowed to become a*

*Wash; drowned in wet seasons when the channels overflow, and turned to grazing in the dryness of summer.*

*I am enfeebled, a slow wraith compared to the pulsing artery that once spawned scores of villages and sustained thousands of simple livelihoods. When rain water from the hills finally reaches the northern end of the channels at Denver, my waters join again. I become the majestic power that flows through Lynn haven, and to my reunion with the sea.*

*The men who stole my waters by their two channels were themselves in the ground before my peatlands shrivelled from lack of water. The rich soil begot from primordial herbage is now sunk far below my river bed. Rain, unable to drain upwards, is held captive on the low fields.*

*The wind gains strength.*

*I shiver under a darkening sky.*

*I am a mercuric shroud.*

*The land is dead.*

At the southern end of the two Bedford Rivers at Hermitage Sluice, Hyde Page points out a damaged sluice gate where water escapes to low ground. They go on to where the River Grant (now the Cam) joins and to the east, water stands for miles towards Soham.

The men move smartly, coaxing their horses along slippery banks. Ely Cathedral looms through a curtain of drizzle as they reach a night's ease. Next day they canter north to Littleport where banks are more robust, passing the Mildenhall River (now the Lark) which extends towards Bury St. Edmunds, although bargemen here still strain to keep a gang of vessels moving under sail and horsepower. The next stretch up to the Brandon River (now the Little Ouse) to Thetford is well embanked up to where the Stoke River (now the Wissey) joins, just before they reach Denver Sluice.

Hyde Page tells the cadets that when the Bedford Rivers were cut about 120 years ago, a sluice was built to reduce the force of the tides in the old river that flooded villages upriver to Earith. Before long, that sluice was smashed to smithereens by fresh water coming down from the counties meeting a very high tide from Lynn. Only its brick foundation remains as an underwater hurdle. Another sluice was built, stronger than the first, but it slows the river and obstructs barges.

He explains that freshwater from higher ground should drain down through the sluice gates when they open as the tide ebbs, but the height of the tides against the gates, even in the ebb, often keeps them closed. This reduces the river's power to scour loose sands back to the sea and over time the sands build up, making the river bed shallow.

The cadets notice the present sluice gate is only half as wide as the river's span, and the gap is encumbered with brushwood. Although there is a small gate for barges to pass, this too is frequently closed.

From Downham Market they head towards Lynn, pausing at Wiggenhall St. Germans. Here a fragile wooden bridge stubbornly resists the energy of tides pushing against its struts. It barely serves the volume of traffic it attracts, being the nearest bridge to Kings Lynn, but it is presently the only alternative to Lynn's ferries.

They look across fields that are flat to the horizon, with only the spires of a flock of churches rising high. The banks here are badly decayed, worn down by hundreds of horses pulling barges with cargo to and from Lynn.

Beyond, Hyde Page and his party reach Eau Brink Hall. The river bends to the west at the start of a semi-circular course which closes in on a narrower path at the approach to Lynn haven.

Here is a silvery lake, three quarters of a mile wide, Hyde Page says, but in summer, it recedes leaving sand shoals so high at low tide that a man could hide behind them. Then, barges have to wait for the next tide to provide enough depth to float, while water lazes on drowned land nearby.

Wind straight off the North Sea bites the cadets who ask Hyde Page how embankments can be made to withstand such violent tides as must be here.

'At first sight, it seems unlikely,' he says, 'but if waters are constricted within a narrower channel, they have more force to increase the scour and take sands back to sea. Banks can be built on the dry shores in summer, but not so close as to be narrower than the river at each end, because that will create more violent currents and deposit more sands.'

'But can embankments be built on shifting sands?' they ask. Hyde Page smiles. It seems they are learning something useful from this exercise.

'I believe they can,' he tells them. 'They need strong protection with fascines taken well down beneath the water to resist rot. Banks must be high too, on both sides, to shelter waters from cross winds which whip up waves that tear into soft mud with incomputable force. Once controlled, the river will deepen its own course, so long as it can flow freely to sea beyond the haven, and even that will improve with time. It would be the quickest, cheapest and safest solution.

'What of Mr. Kinderley's plan for a new Cut from Wiggenhall St. Germans straight to Lynn to bypass this curve completely?'

'In some ways it answers the problem, but there's no guarantee it will work as imagined in theory. It will not temper the force of waters coming down the river in winter, and it could create great hazards for ships in the harbour. The winding course achieves that end, but even now, fierce tides can make ships break loose from their moorings. It wouldn't be my recommendation.'

Hyde Page is not just an engineer who knows how to manage flowing water. He is a strategist and prospers by learning who owns the land, who wants to occupy it and what each wants to achieve. He knows whose voices need to be heard and whose opinion of his success will be heard at the pinnacle of government, in whose fickle hands his own livelihood rests.

At Lynn, Hyde Page visits Alderman John Cary, Mayor of the King's Lynn Corporation, at his mansion on Chequer Street (now King Street). Cary is distracted from his usual run of thought by the machinations of the Bedford Level Corporation. They've resurrected Kinderley's old plan for a Cut to carry the river in a straight line to Lynn harbour and its path is directly across his estate. More, he is married to Elizabeth Harwick, whose father owns Eau Brink Hall. They both get their fresh water by a channel which could be blocked off by this Cut and their road connection could be severed as well. Cary demands to know from Hyde Page what works are involved.

'There are no firm decisions at present. Lord Townshend requires to know of the situation here now, to better inform his considerations.'

Cary smoulders in frustration. This Hyde Page is obviously one of Bedford's men, concealing what he knows. Some in high quarters acknowledge the Bedford Level Corporation is a shambles, but in his own experience, what the Bedford Level Corporation plan, they get, by some means or another.

'Well, what will you tell him?'

'That the river is frequently obstructed, the banks are generally very poor, and from what I've seen already, the harbour is treacherously silted, even just here across from West Lynn.'

'Yes, yes, we know that,' Cary snaps. 'What do you propose?'

'There would be a major improvement if the banks were built higher, or at least securely repaired, along the whole length of the Great Ouse from Earith, to improve scouring and deepen the riverbed.'

'No, no, no, that won't suffice. The banks will be decayed in a season. What of Denver Sluice? Did you see that? What do you think to that?'

'When embankment is established all along on both sides of the river, the necessity for Denver Sluice should be reconsidered. It may not be necessary.'

'Is that the extent of your expert considerations? We'll wait a long time before your trust in embanking comes to fruit,' Cary retorts. 'And what of the proposed new Cut?' he probes again.

'I recommend embankment first, then a re-evaluation before deciding whether to spend so much money.'

'Embankment! I say again, those who know the tides here will tell you it has no chance of success. My family have kept up embankments on our land against the river for years, but one bad flood and they are destroyed. Embankment will not work.'

'With respect, sir, a military approach would be to constrict the river on both banks at a suitable width and for considerable distance, so that the most forceful of the transverse waves do not develop. Waters go deep then rather than wide.'

'Are you saying I don't know how to erect embankments?'

'No, sir, certainly not. But work of the nature needed here requires a workforce who can complete all the construction in a single season. The banks also have to be protected by robust fascines, which military engineers have perfected over the years. We depend on them to get armies across flooded terrain and we have to work quickly. They will, of course, eventually need repair, but in the meantime the banks will have encouraged the flow to deepen the bed of the river all the way to the outlet. The forces working on the banks will gradually reduce. That would be the right time to consider a Cut, if one is still needed. Embankment will require less land than a Cut so the whole venture would be cheaper.'

'Cheaper, quite possibly, but useless. Denver Sluice is the problem, and Lord Townshend needs to deal with it, but I suppose if you can offer any alternative, it would be some improvement to this desperate scheme,' Cary replies grudgingly. 'I hope you will leave Lord Townshend in no doubt as to my personal sentiments. As for the King's Lynn Corporation, you'll be aware that we have long-standing obligations to His Majesty's Admiralty for maintaining a safe channel for shipping from the estuary to Wiggenhall St. Germans. We intend to honour those obligations in full. We will be robust in objecting to this Cut for it will ruin the harbour for certain.'

'Any engineer will tell you that in a new Cut, the dimensions are critical to ensure efficacy and safety but I will give him your views, sir.'

A courier arrives at Hyde Page's lodgings with a message from Lord Townshend. High tide or low, Hyde Page must return to London. With no means of travel before next morning, Hyde Page accompanies some seagoing captains to the lower harbour and its anchorage for larger ships, and the outfall into the wide North Sea, completing his survey.

They return to Lynn at dusk, and away to London at dawn. From there, Hyde Page departs for Portsmouth to embark on HMS Cerberus for Boston, Massachusetts, and Bunker's Hill.

*Men will ignore me while they are at war on distant seas. God speed, wise and valiant Redcoat. Fare thee well.*

## Ely
### November 1775

The Corporation faces criticism from every corner of the Bedford Level. Landowning gentry come from as far as Northampton to Suffolk and from Earith to the Wash. The Bedford Level once stretched to Peterborough and Lincolnshire, originally called the North Level, which had separated from the Bedford Level Corporation decades previously. Now only the Middle and South Levels remain, roughly south from the River Nene, with coastal Marshland tucked between there and the Great Ouse, towards Wisbech and Downham Market. Many hundreds of acres here are owned by more distant estates, whose absentee owners remain entitled to attend Bedford Level Corporation meetings.

King Charles I judged the entire area a drowned waste and coveted it for productive land if it could be drained. The Earl of Bedford and other investors, called Adventurers, agreed to finance and manage the project. The deal was they could have about a third of the area, ninety-five thousand acres, called Adventurers' land, on which they could charge taxes, but about half of the tax collected was to be reserved for maintenance. The remaining two thirds, which was not to be taxed, was called Freeland. Changes to this had to be approved by Parliament.

In November at Ely, everybody agrees something must be done to improve drainage and navigation. There are scores of opinions on how to achieve it. But, the Chairman says, they cannot pay for more work, or even continue what they're already doing, without raising taxes. They need to restructure finances, he says, or the Level will return to waste. To do that, they need Parliamentary authority in a new Act. They intend to start the process with a detailed petition that states the case plainly. Nobody is satisfied with this vague aim, but without more detail, there can be no useful argument.

When it is published, the petition causes outrage in Lynn. It proposes a general tax of six pence an acre each year to be charged on all the Adventurers' and Freelands, and two pence an acre on all common land within them, for no more than seven years, to pay for general drainage. Adventurers' land is to pay more, a tax and a half, plus another six pence an acre depending on the quality of the soil.

All goods carried to and from Wisbech and Lynn by water will be subject to a toll, the amount to be agreed between the Bedford Level Corporation and the merchants. Monies raised will pay for works to improve the outfall to the sea by such methods as proposed years ago by Mr. Kinderley.

There is uproar in the merchant's Exchange. The landowners are to pay taxes for only seven years, while the navigation pays in perpetuity? To a man, the merchants, town councils and bargemen up and down the river say 'Never!'

## Inns of Court, London
## Spring 1776

Lord Townshend arrives early at the Fen Office in Lincoln's Inn, conveniently situated for the Bedford Level Corporation's numerous members who are lawyers, Ministers of Parliament or resident in their London houses. He wants a moment with Registrar Charles Nalson Cole before the myriad concerns of Bedford Level meetings take hold of his concentration.

'Have you heard anything in reaction to the Bill in the Fens?'

'As you predicted, the trading interests are protesting vigorously, but some are against it simply because they don't believe the Corporation has run out of funds. They say they can't see the benefit of what we say has already been spent.'

'Ridiculous! The place would return to a pestilential bog if we did nothing. Do they expect us to lay out our accounts? Do they accuse us of personal profit?'

'I've heard no suggestion of that, but some are trying to determine how their taxes have been used. Not knowing what has been done, or the details of what is planned for the future, makes them suspicious.'

'We won't get any sense from most of them. They'd rather see the place a wasteland than co-operate. We should do what we can to quiet the opposition and smooth the Bill's passage into law. Look into the records and sketch out the headlines. Add something conciliatory and persuasive of the good sense of the new Bill, and get it circulated to the towns promptly.'

Cole struggles. The more he looks at the fading records, the more he realises that the river always wins in the end, no matter whose expert opinion is given or whose wisdom makes decisions. He concludes that the Bedford Level men seem compelled to dig holes and pour their treasure into them.

Cole brings his skills as an accomplished lawyer and supreme diplomat to his task. All men have a duty, he writes, to contribute to this debate. Hindsight reveals that much effort and expenditure has been fruitless, for the land is still submerged, even more now than in years past. The previous ideas must have seemed practicable and likely to be effective at the time they were decided upon, but Cole observes that even Cornelius Vermuyden himself, the legendary drainage champion, was hampered by parsimonious funds. He ignored his own principles of drainage when he decided to divide the waters of the Great Ouse and reduced costs by not raising high enough embankments. Since then, the same inadequate principles have applied to every new undertaking.

Cole appeals to his readers' collective heritage. 'Are we bound to repeat the mistakes of the past? Is it in our hands that the land will return to bog? We need a new approach, or we will lose it all.'

Within weeks, Lord Townshend receives a dispatch from Massachusetts, including a map of the approaches to Boston harbour. Hyde Page is injured, but chooses to recover from amputation of his foot in America rather than face the voyage to England. The Bedford Level Corporation will have to find another engineer with experience and an open mind.

*Now comes William Elstobb, surveyor and teacher of Mathematics. He rows here, there, never resting. I know him. I heard his first squawking cry from his father's sailmaking business on the Boal Quay at Lynn. He knows my tides as well as most. He talks in rods and poles, never in fathoms, for he is a land man, not a mariner.*

*He has no liking for orders from any man. When old Richard Dunthorne dies before he's finished the new Cut on the River Nene below Wisbech, works supervisor Elstobb steps up to complete the task to the satisfaction of all. Elstobb hopes this, along with his previous work in the Bedford Level, puts him in a premier position to replace Dunthorne as Superintendent General of the Bedford Level*

*Corporation. But James Golborne, nephew of John from Chester, both highly reputable waterway engineers, finds favour with the Duke of Bedford by draining at his lands at Thorney, and Elstobb is a disappointed man.*

Elstobb is contracted to survey the Great Ouse instead. He is a man of strong opinions, and not shy of communicating his thoughts on the revival of Kinderley's plan for a Cut to straighten the river above Lynn. It will be an advantage, he pronounces, and all persons interested in trade and commerce would surely agree, provided they could be fully satisfied that they will obtain the advantage that Mr. Kinderley says will arise from it. But, Elstobb cautions, some able engineers disagree. They think such a Cut would be prejudicial. Others think that it is unnecessary, and that the present channel might be amended at less expense, so as to answer the needs of draining as well as navigation. Elstobb believes that a Cut must result in a quicker fall for the water in a more confined course resulting in improved drainage and navigation.

## The River Great Ouse
## Summer 1776

James Creassy comes forward to offer a new opinion on the drainage. He is a Fenland man who has worked with the most experienced engineers like John Grundy Jr. and Langley Edwards of King's Lynn, who improved the drainage and navigation of Holland Low Fen and the River Witham into Boston, Lincolnshire.

Creassy suggests that what he did in Holland Low Fen would be effective further south. Fresh upland water should be diverted in a system of drains that join up with the tidal Great Ouse just above Lynn. Two sluices placed near Lynn could keep out very high tides and maintain river levels for navigation, with flood embankments throughout. Both tidal and fresh waters will flow without causing each other to back up, preventing their escape through porous banks.

'Take experience as your future guide,' Creassy suggests to all noblemen and gentlemen interested in draining the area. 'Don't depend on the fallacious and ill-grounded reports of self-interested and designing men whose business has always been to emphasise the difficulties of general drainage so that they might more readily fatten upon the spoils of the country by multiplying jobs for themselves. Among those vultures of society that have infested this part of the country are the engine builders and jobbing engineers who have combined together, to the almost total ruin of the landed interest in these Fens. See for yourselves how the Holland Fen rivers are higher than the land around them, but the land is dry and productive. Where people once walked across the river bed at low tide without getting wet-shod, now large ships can float at ease.'

Creassy shows his plan to Elstobb, who raises several objections, but each time Creassy explains how these same problems were overcome in Holland Fen. Elstobb remains resolutely of his own mind.


### The River Great Ouse
### Winter 1776

> *I know their secrets. I pass by the hulls of their craft and hear their babble. I sense the effort in their grunts when they work their boats and the sighs of those lying together in their bunks. I hear chatter in the hostelries and the call of the humans working in the fields. I wince at the wails of children crying out in the silence of night. I nod at those breathing their last before dawn and I know whose pens are dipped in malice.*

Lord Townshend is aggrieved. For each experienced engineer's report, the next contradicts it. Anonymous pamphlets create waves of public invective. Each writer claims his version of history is correct; each land agent's response to flooding is more practical; each armchair surveyor has a better view of the slope as the river approaches its outfall to the sea. Each proves, without a shadow of doubt, that their particular approach to draining is the one sensible path.

The Bedford Level Board takes sides and little ground is gained, but Cole's financial accounts force the reality of near bankruptcy upon them. Corporation honour depends on finding a way forward and it is the Board's duty to implement it. They direct Superintendent General James Golborne to settle the engineering question by making his own survey, and they devise a formula for taxing which is intended to bridge over the current bellicose attitudes at all levels

Lord Townshend hopes one pamphlet or another might induce more rational thought. By good fortune, one highly persuasive Impartial Proprietor supplies just what is needed.

The purpose of the pamphlet, the Proprietor says, is to supply information which the public had been promised, but which had not been forthcoming. He sympathises with all parties and, like Cole, bemoans the lack of detail on which taxpayers with ruined fields might judge future proposals.

He includes a reprinting of the observations of Lt. Hyde Page and Mr. Creassy, saying both were impartial as neither would benefit from a share in the work they recommended. The Impartial Proprietor addresses his readers, saying their two systems do not entirely coincide, but each may contain useful matter and readers can adopt what is best.

The Impartial Proprietor is, he assures readers, not accusing anyone of neglect, but past experience warns that new propositions and powers should be considered with great circumspection. It is sufficient, he says, for any intelligent and unbiased man to look for a moment at those ill-placed, ill-proportioned, stupendous, tottering constructions at the end of the Ouse Washes.

Add to this other works, similar in merit and execution: expensive sluices which neither open nor shut; indulgencies of running wide drains into small ones and of draining one level at the expense of another. Above all, that long-noted nuisance Denver Sluice which, like an ill-shapen gigantic bully posted in the avenue of a public place, insults the public merely because no one has the courage to remove him.

These instances of useless and expensive works entitle you, the reader, to receive the fullest information and assurance that we shall not remain the annual sacrifice to ignorant engineers and accommodating directors.

The Impartial Proprietor is inclined to think that if the Corporation and trading interests of Lynn are given a clear proposition for the recovery of the river, one that is founded on undeniable principles, with the works clearly estimated, costed and planned, then the trade of Lynn would hardly wish to trample under-foot the feeble fence of the poor occupier of land without paying a fair proportion for the advantages the trade would receive.

The advocates of this Bill should explain sufficiently, the Proprietor concludes, if they wish to engage both the landed and trading interests. They should propose nothing without the fullest information and attempt nothing by means of management or power.

A perfect bullseye, Lord Townshend thinks.

Cambridge men take a different approach. They send their objections to the House of Commons in a petition based on the financial impacts of the proposed Bill.

"The tonnage of one shilling a chauldron (about one and a half tons) and a shilling a ton on other goods, is unreasonable, partial and unjust. Cambridge has been obliged to procure a separate Act of Parliament to preserve the navigation from Clayhithe (near Earith) which laid an additional burden on all goods coming to Cambridge; it is good navigation now, and requires no more amendment. No improvement will enable water men to bring coals and other merchandise cheaper than they do now, and the expense intended by this Bill will be carried mostly by poor people.

If this Bill is passed, an annual sum of £8,000 will be raised, and the tolls from the intended tonnage will raise £20,000 more. The toll on goods coming from Lynn up the rivers Ouse and Grant is made perpetual, whereas the tax on fen lands is for only seven years. This will enable the Adventurers to pay off their present enormous debt, to their own benefit, but leave the burden of maintaining the works upon the trade to Cambridge from Lynn.

Your petitioners humbly apprehend that the laying of a tax on the public for the improvement of the estates of individuals is unprecedented and unjust."

### The River Great Ouse
### Spring 1777

*I watch them pass. The barges carry men who are organised and single-minded. They compute their destinations with the change of the seasons and the turn of the sun, with the day of the week for their markets and the calendar of saints for their fairs, for the fattening of animals or the harvest of the fields and seas. Their boats are their schools, their fingers are their tallies and their ears are their books. Their custom is their law and they are ever vigilant to my currents.*

*In summer, when the horizon lightens, the gangs are ready and scuttle out of the fleets, securing their position on me like hunting parties of ebony water beetles. They're quiet, each man in his place, attending to his task. Hundreds of them every day shadow my waters, depending on their computation. Fishermen return from the ocean with a catch ready to pack into barrels for the next day's barges. Later, more graceful vessels move with white sails, some for the sheer joy of being with me.*

*In winter, barges flit in short hops, more warily, for nobody battles the fresh waters and wind without good reason.*

## House of Parliament, London
## Spring 1777

A Parliamentary committee is convened to examine evidence. The first witness is engineer Thomas Hogard, for many years Surveyor for Deeping Fen in Lincolnshire, who describes the area of the Bedford Level. Then John Wing, surveyor and steward to the Duke of Bedford at Thorney, confirms that both the Adventurers' lands and Freeland are equally likely to be overflowed.

Mr. Cole, the Registrar, says that the last tax and a half on the Middle and South Levels produced about £6,500 a year. Taxes on the Adventurers' lands are now so high that increasingly the land is let go and taken back by the Corporation to be auctioned. This now amounts to at least 10,000 acres. Mr. Cole says debts stand at £38,000.

Mr. Hogard says great quantities of water are conveyed to the sea, but it does not increase the stream or deepen rivers because it spills out where banks are not kept up. There are nearly 200 miles of banks, and he thinks it is necessary to embank them all. If that were done, it would still be necessary to have drains to convey waters to the rivers. He estimates £180,000 is needed, which includes £28,000 for Kinderley's Cut.

Mr. Hogard adds that if the rivers are embanked, the floods might rise in them higher than they do now, but they would run off sooner. If the land is lost, the costs of recovery would be ten times more than keeping it drained. The costs of preserving the navigation by tolls, if undertaken now, would be less than the extra costs that will arise if navigation is jeopardised.

Denver Sluice is not, in his opinion, an obstruction to the waters of the South Level. He thinks the river is worse now because changes to agriculture and highways result in more water draining more quickly into rivers, whereas before it lay and evaporated. Windmills also throw more mud into the rivers and the new navigations that have opened up to Biggleswade and Northampton mean the rivers need to be deeper, and the banks higher to resist flood.

The committee ask Mr. Cole how the gentlemen of the Board of the Corporation go about their duties. Cole replies that they take great trouble and go to personal expense to undertake it with fidelity, justice and attention. He says that when he went to the April meeting at Ely in 1773, he passed through a countryside almost overflowed from Cambridge to Ely. Nothing could equal the distress he saw. The streets were crowded with labourers demanding their wages to feed their families, and the members of the Board who were present subscribed over £1,000 of their own money to pay them, because there were no more funds.

A surveyor from Littleport says heavier horses are now used to pull larger barges over mud in shallower water. Six pence a horse is charged for passing between Prickwillow and Littleport to repair the damage done, which could wear away the banks by two foot a year. Journeys that used to take eight hours now take nearly a week because water is so low at Littleport.

A merchant from Peterborough emphasises the practical delays. He used to carry eighty chauldrons, around 120 tons of coal, with one gang of barges, but has reduced this to thirty chauldrons to avoid going aground. He says it takes ten days now to get from Peterborough to Morton's Leam near Wisbech, which used to be done in eight hours. He used to carry coal for one shilling and six pence a chauldron, but now has to charge two shillings and six pence to make ends meet.

The caretaker of the banks on the One Hundred Foot River says banks are damaged by droves taking cattle from Norfolk to St. Ives market, sometimes up to a hundred black cattle a week for three months of the year.

'Gentlemen', the Commons committee Chairman announces, 'it is the opinion of this committee that the drainage and navigation of this vast country must inevitably be lost, unless both the Freelands and Navigation contribute to the relief of the Adventurers.' Accordingly, when this report returns to the House of Commons, the area's MPs, who also happen to be members of the Bedford Level Corporation, are instructed to prepare a Bill for the Commons to consider.

At a meeting in April at Ely, the Corporation are given three cost estimates varying from £145,000 to £185,000. The Corporation decide to amend the Bill in response to costs and once more they become bogged down in argument. It is not presented to Parliament to be read a second time and is finally lost.

The jubilation in Lynn and Cambridge is not shared in the Board room of the Bedford Level Corporation. They had tried to placate, they reason, but as ever, their efforts were rejected. It was questionable enough that their own Mr. Cole had been lukewarm in his answers to the committee, though he had clearly tried to be fair. A few murmur between themselves about his early retirement, but Lord Townshend decides that the man is a servant who does a decent job, and after all, nobody has died or been slandered.

A heftier blow is another anonymous pamphlet which appears in the summer. It accuses the Board of complacency and questions their very existence. The Board is composed of eminently honourable men, it says, but has always been based on a false reasoning; that under its terms, funds could ever be sufficient for the work required. It should be broken up and reconstituted with representatives from all interested parties.

More, it said that the Bill being proposed by the Bedford Level Corporation is illegal. Its own constitution does not allow funds to be raised by taxing beyond the 40,000 acres originally reserved for the purpose. No man should support this Bill because it serves nobody's interests. A formula for raising sufficient funds from all parties is thoughtfully provided.

If only it might be so easy, Lord Townshend thinks.

Then a rumour spreads that the author is one of their own, Soame Jenyns himself. Suspicion falls on him because he frequently publishes his own deeply philosophical ramblings. If he is the author, his ancestors would be turning in their graves.

Lord Townshend had seen the appalling state of the river above Soham when he accompanied Creassy as he was completing his survey. There is no doubt that something needs to be done. Frustrated by contradicting messages from so-called engineers, Lord Townshend decides he needs to have an unbiased account of the state of the rivers and banks from someone who will simply use their eyes and intelligence. Cole can redeem himself over the summer.

**The River Great Ouse**
**Summer 1777**

> *I warm as they sweat, the men in their boats, and scratch at the gnat bites on their pale skins. Rotting vegetation offends those more used to city reeks, but the man Cole and his assistants labour on. He sees where my streams are infested with weeds, my bed nearly dry, my sore banks broken and seeping, and old cuts, once painfully stark but now scabbed and redundant, that divide and weaken me. He knows how much money is applied to my banks. It's expensive to pile them high and make them waterproof with strong clay, but he sees these are the only banks which resist time.*

Cole presents an auditor's view of the works. He sees money wasted in paying for bank repairs which will not last a winter. Soil is thrown over weeds instead of onto firm foundations. Even where men are paid to dig out and deepen the river bed, instead they beat down the soft porous floor with spades and flatten it with their large mallet-like flag-beetles until the banks look higher, but the beds swell again when tides return. Cole sees cursory supervision of working gangs and downright fraud by some.

In some stretches he can sail easily on water unencumbered by weeds, where the Corporation or landowner has been persuaded to hire a Bear machine to dredge right to the bottom of the river bed. This grabs all the plant roots, some as large as a man's thigh, and dumps them as Bear dirt high on the banks. The water flow stays unobstructed for several years afterwards.

Normal rodding to clear weeds twice a year is less expensive, but only removes the tops of weeds. Roots and stems in the river bed still grow in an ever increasing mat of fibres and silt, layer on layer until the bed is so high that summer waters barely flow over them.

Cole reasons this lack of investment contributes to the insupportable maintenance costs which burden the Corporation, and make funding any new works almost impossible.

All of this, bad enough in itself, is overshadowed by the destruction of banks by horses haling barges. Over years, some banks have been worn away by hooves digging into mud and splashing sods into the waters, so much so that the bed of the river has moved and exposed the original foundations of the bank. This leaves an inadequate mound of mud to protect fields from flooding. Some farmers put obstructions on the towing paths to hinder barges and some even manage to get barge owners to pay for the damage, but Cole concludes that most live in perpetual enmity with each other.

The Board receives his report with interest, but gives little consideration to steps they could take to improve their own management. Nothing dissuades them from their obsession to present another petition to Parliament.

## Littleport, Cambridgeshire
## October 1777

Scarlet Browne, lawyer and Lynn's Town Clerk, peeks beyond the window blind in his carriage to see if the rain has eased off. 'It's still pouring,' he grouses to himself.

He is on an errand for the new Mayor of Lynn, attorney Phillip Case, or else he'd have given this trip a miss. He'd left it until the last minute, in the hope that the weather would improve, or at least dry up a little, because after a few days of rain, this road to Ely is notorious for trapping carriages in a quagmire up to the axles.

It has been wet for over two weeks. The sodden fields around Lynn are hung over by a persistent cloud that shifts back and forth by the hour, and the waterways run worryingly high. Out here on the open track between Downham Market and Ely he becomes claustrophobic, hemmed in by an opaque wall with no substance. He can wave his hand through a mist which isn't there, only evidenced by a cold damp which penetrates his glove and chills his fingers. It erases the horizon, disorientating any traveller without a thorough knowledge of the hedges and dykes hereabouts.

Browne is anxious to reach Ely by dusk, and prays the driver has paced the horses to preserve their stamina, but the trials of the journey are quickly forgotten when he reaches his destination. The inns always do good business when the Bedford is in town. He has a chance to renew acquaintances aside a roaring fire, to dine well with pleasant conversation and retire to a dry bed.

Next day, the severity of the continuing rain concerns many of those with riverside properties. A cold wind hustles them all into the Shire Hall for a mid-morning meeting, but none of the Board arrives. Someone says they're at The Lamb down the road, interrogating Soame Jenyns.

On his return to Lynn, Browne tells Mayor Case that in the afternoon, Cole presented the findings of his summer visit. The gentlemen present were not surprised that the Corporation is in debt if they manage funds as badly as his report indicated. Then Cole outlined a draft of a new Bill.

'The main differences are that the Adventurers' lands will be charged a double tax, at one shilling and sixpence an acre for seven years, to pay for the expenses involved in the passage of a Bill through Parliament, then to pay for interest on the debt, then about £2,000 a year towards works.

'Traders will pay one shilling a ton of merchandise, or on each chauldron of coal. This would be sixpence at Downham Bridge and sixpence at the entrance of whatever river they take afterwards. The Corporation will invest the tolls towards Denver Sluice, which they want to rebuild, and they will borrow £75,000 on the security of this income.'

'That's ambitious for a Corporation that's on its knees in debt,' Mayor Case comments.

'Yes, and they propose to tax the Freelands as well, at nine pence an acre for three years certain, then at a rate graduated by its value, for ever. This nine pence is claimed to be equal to one shilling of tonnage, to pay for works under the direction of Commissioners chosen by the landowners.'

'There's no hope of a new constitution for the Bedford Level Corporation as Soame Jenyns suggests, then?' Mayor Case asks.

'That was not mentioned, but they're suggesting the tax on tonnage should be dealt with by separate Commissioners, who should include the Mayors of Lynn and Cambridge. They also propose to regulate haling.'

'Is this saving face, or a genuine attempt for conciliation, do you think?'

'Determining the motives of the Corporation is never easy, so at this point I couldn't say,' Browne answers. 'Lord Townshend asked me if I thought there would be further opposition from the gentlemen in trade. I said the terms which Mr. Cole read out seemed more likely to be agreeable to the traders. I reminded them that the merchants had said they would agree to a perpetual tax of sixpence a ton if a sixpence tax were perpetual on the Freelands as well. I said the traders I knew would expect the Bill to include a body to control collecting the haling revenues and paying for damages.'

'Quite so. What then?'

'Some said they thought we only wanted to throw stumbling blocks in their way as usual. The gentlemen of Cambridge and Bury St. Edmunds agreed with me though.'

'What of Kinderley's Cut from Eau Brink?'

'They didn't specify any intention, but I don't think that means they've given up the hope of making it. They may intend to use the power of the former Acts. Afterwards, I was invited to take dinner with the Board, and heard that James Golborne, their Superintendent General is about to make a report, on which they intend to rely. A letter from him was read out, and he says that all efforts will be in vain unless they make the Cut as Kinderley proposed. He has also designed another drain and outfall for Marshland.'

Mayor Case summarises. 'So, they want to ignore their own rules, tax everyone in sight and spend a fortune on destroying our harbour, despite all we've said, and they're going to use Parliament to do it?'

'It seems so, yes.'

The two lawyers exchange a grimace.

'Sharpen your quill, Scarlet. There is much more to do.'

When James Golborne's report appears in December, he says he and his uncle John Golborne had viewed a great length of the River Great Ouse and its tributaries. Even in the height of summer, they found misery and desolation throughout the region, with deserted fields underwater as far as they could see.

Where the river was wide it was also shallow and prone to flood. Some bridges were less than half the width of the river above them which naturally overflowed in heavy rain. They calculated the descent of the river towards the outfall, and the strength of the tide that reached shallower parts, and from that deduced the power of the ebb to scour silt back to the sea and deepen the river bed.

The strength of the tide fell dramatically near Wiggenhall St. Germans, where it spread over the shallows, and what was needed there was a narrower channel. This would be a great advantage to navigation; traders would no longer be delayed waiting for higher tides. They would be able to get from Lynn to Denver Sluice on one tide with loaded barges, and they wouldn't need river pilots who charge up to nine shillings a trip.

This remedy would be cheaper for the Bedford Level Corporation to fund because there would be a shorter distance to embank. The surface level of the water would be reduced by about four foot, and in effect, banks would rise by four foot throughout. The tide would flow higher upstream and flow longer on its ebb.

The Golbornes were against raising embankments in general, especially in the water-bound South Level where the ground was so porous that water would penetrate underneath any new bank, resulting in more breeches. They returned repeatedly to removing the obstruction at Wiggenhall St. Germans to recover an adequate outfall to sea. The problem was not caused by Denver Sluice, they said, for even if this were taken down, the outfall would not be recovered.

James Golborne estimated that the works required would cost about £38,000. Previous estimates reached over £167,000. The saving would be enough for any smaller work that seemed necessary after the Cut was in place. One such might be improving the towpaths to reduce the distance in places between the bank and the river, where horses pull at angles which severely damage the bank and cause great stress to the animals when their tormenters will not let them rest.

Scarlet Browne, Phillip Case and all the merchants of Lynn inspect the twenty two page report carefully. They look in vain for any mention of measures to counteract the known danger of unmoderated torrents arriving full force in Lynn's haven. On the wharves and in the Fleets, ship captains and bargemen fume in resentment.

## The River Great Ouse
## January 1779

*I study them as they swagger about in the rooms of human power. They give a nod here, a smile there, a witty remark, but none of them know what it is to live on me, to master my channels and provide food for their families. These men think they can dominate me from the comfort of their snugs. They are absurd fools. They anger me.*

*I beckon wind from the north. Heavy clouds converge under cover of darkness. There's no moon, no stars. Rain pummels the fields and raging brooks sprout between men's houses.*

*I gather, coming full downstream from the high country and meet the tide rushing in from the sea. Boats rise on their bellies and tug at their anchors, then shatter down on sand and stone. Some are thrown beyond, past the shore into fields to lie with broken backs.*

*Wind finds the ducts in shacks and mansions. It rips their coverings and tears their walls.*

*And I spread, with a rapturous abandon of rare delight.*

*I loosen my stays. I disperse and penetrate.*

*I grab the trees they rammed in my side and throw them downstream. Their platforms collapse. Their lights fizzle out. Their oars are as nought to my power.*

*I sweep land animals off their puny legs, and they are dragged down by sodden coats. They swim against their nature. They fail.*

*Men howl in terror, losing grip of their children, their*
*voices silent against the roar of the wind.*
*I am strong.*
*I am free.*
*I rampage.*
*I explode.*
*I roar.*
*I swirl over their green shoots and strip soil that*
*clogs their drains.*
*I infest their cellars and undermine their walls. I drag*
*mortar from their bricks.*
*Licking, sucking, pushing, harder, harder still,*
*deeper, deeper still, until their walls tumble.*

People appear from the alleys of Lynn and gape at the destruction of the night. Wharves are destroyed. Roofs and corners are torn off buildings. The river, calm now as if the storm had never happened, is full of debris. No vessel has been spared. Those empty of cargo were tossed about like tinder. Some are smashed beyond saving, sitting now with foul brown water past their bows. Barges and lighters that still float need repair. Ditches have overflowed and spread their corruption. A noxious odour begins to rise from the streets.

As reports come from upriver, the full scale of the devastation becomes clear. Banks are breached, and when the tide rises again, more saltwater will pour into the fields for miles around. Crops are ruined and many animals lost. Sheep carcases are everywhere, and the occasional drowned cow and pig. Cottages and shacks are razed, forcing labourers and their families to take refuge in churches and barns. Store houses are knee deep in water. Very little clean food remains.

Small groups of silent Fenlanders pick up what remains of their homes. Already, sheets of sailcloth are being fixed to what supports still stand. They'll soon be in the town begging for food, but they will not be dislodged from their land by any damn flood

# Part Two
# The Worrying

# Part Two
# The Worrying

### The River Great Ouse
### 1781

*I am tranquil now. The men who would control me turn elsewhere to defend their country from foreign threat. Their honour and fortunes are challenged by forces they imagine greater than I can muster. Some march in fine glittery uniforms behind squeaky fife and hollow drums. Together they present a sunshine mettle but it will fade on silent shores in winter fog because they are too few to protect their towns from a true invasion. Their leaders are distant, immersed in tactics that don't trouble me.*

### Queen Square, London
### December 1782

The Reverend John Towers Allen, curate of Wiggenhall St. Mary Magdalen, and his wife Mary are visiting her father Charles Turner at his smart new house in London's Queen Square.

Charles Turner had been the Collector of Customs for the port of King's Lynn, assisted by his deputy John Jaspar Vancouver, whose young son George had entranced them with tales of sailing the South Seas with Captain James Cook to learn more of the Southern Continent and the Hawaiian Islands. Between Charles Turner's walls, all manner of well-informed news is shared, on exploration, trade and the London theatre which was Charles's great enthusiasm. The state of King's Lynn's river and Marshland drainage are rarely off the agenda.

Turner reveals that James Watt, inventor of steam pumps, has been commissioned to install a steam engine near Rotterdam, to test the claim that it will eliminate dependence on wind and water powered mills, so water can still be moved from low ground up into the drains if the wind drops.

'Will such an engine even work? Draining flat land is surely different from lifting water from a mineshaft?' Reverend Towers Allen asks. 'What happens if an engine replaces a windmill or two and then it breaks down? At least windmills can be relied upon to work most of the time. The risk of flood if all drainage is lost cannot be countenanced, surely? But it would be astonishing if such a machine would drain Marshland,' he muses.

'Yes, and Watt claims it uses only a fraction of the fuel needed by the old Newcomen pumps in the Cornish mines,' Turner says. 'I understand the parts can be made locally from Watt's drawings. He just charges his costs for that, to reduce the start-up cost. His profit comes through payments on a licence based on a third of the cost saving on fuel, compared to a Newcomen pump doing the same work, for as long as the patent runs. But his firm are the only ones supplying the valves, and the men experienced in assembling the pumps, so in the end it probably costs as much.'

'Mine owners can set costs against gains from copper and the like. There's less incentive where there's no product to sell immediately. It'd be a problem to recover profits from agriculture around Lynn. I'm curious about the costs involved. Let's make enquiries,' Turner suggests.

The following day, John Towers Allen and his father-in-law set down what seems to them to be reasonable questions in the light of their knowledge of Fenland drains and the demands of mine shafts.

'We need to shift large quantities of water quite quickly, but not as high as in a mine, rather than small quantities, very high, continually.'

'Ask how much water can be raised, shall we say, ten feet, in a given time?'

'And the price of coals to run it. Tell him Newcastle coals. And ask for a sketch. If it sounds reasonable, we'll send it along to Lynn.'

Watt replies without delay, in a four sheet letter detailing his charging policy and broad estimates of what might be required. He thinks that for a ten foot lift, an engine with a cylinder diameter of about forty-eight inches working at ten strokes per minute will suffice. This will shift about 2,000 cubic feet of water per minute.

The general cost of the engine will be about £2,500, and a third of the saving compared with a Newcomen engine will be about seven bushels of coal an hour, to be paid quarterly.

Turner and Reverend Towers Allen compute this rate, compare it to the much lower costs of wind and water power, and conclude they should wait to discover if the Dutch experiment is successful.

## The River Great Ouse
## Summer 1788

*I hear whimpers on the wind from across the North Sea. Men watch, alert to the spate of strangers arriving in fear of their lives. First come the rainbow people with their fortunes in portmanteaux carried by servants. Then the white-collared men in black frocks with go-everywhere eyes, humble clerics they say, who preach at the gates of our naval dockyards. Then the middling, unkempt and footsore, with only what they stand in.*

*They leave piteous scrags, forced from their meagre lives by calls for a freedom that enslaves or kills them. So many that guillotines take four, then seven at a time, till only the gravediggers and fanatics remain. Then these march north into the lands of our allies, and they vow to conquer my shore too, before they are still.*

*But my own foes are already here. They rise from
my banks and grow ever stronger.*

## The Fen Office, Inns of Court, London
## 1788

Lord Townshend, now raised to Marquess by the King and
retired from his duties as Master of Ordnance, looks about
him at the assembled Board of the Bedford Level Corporation
with irritation. Order is in danger of breaking down in
France. The lower classes have become emboldened by the
American revolution against the British for representation
or independence. A movement for similar rights is gaining
ground among those who would end the exorbitant whims
of the French King and his court. Unrest is spreading
indiscriminately, sharpened by poor harvests and hunger.

Here, the King demands that past and present military
should contribute to defending the country, as much in his
defence against his own subjects as the French, in case the
peasantry here embrace a similar passion for insurrection.
Lord Townshend feels stirrings of excitement in his guts and
he longs to be somewhere else, discussing military campaigns
with seasoned warriors like himself.

Retirement from the Bedford Level Corporation is not
an option, elderly though he is. Members stay to the death.
Although there are some useful newer members, there are too
few bright sparks with enough experience to affect matters at
hand. The young Francis, Duke of Bedford, has just reached his
majority but his lawyer and mentor, Robert Palmer, has passed
on. In his place, the family have pressed John Wing, surveyor
and steward for the Russell estates at Thorney to join the Board
of the Corporation. Reverend George Jenyns, Soame Jenyns's
successor at Bottisham, has also stepped up.

Lord Townshend suspects that Francis might need him.
Some of the Conservators had caught the scent of French
unrest and had tried to resist Francis taking his hereditary

position as Governor. Although the boy is willing enough, he seems hesitant. The last time Lord Townshend felt as anxious as the boy looks today was as a young cadet blanching before his first active engagement, before a slap on the back from a veteran solider stiffened his resolve. Lord Townshend will offer the young Duke a discreet but firm guiding hand. There is no doubt though, that some measure must be taken to save the Corporation sinking into bankruptcy and financial disgrace for them all.

Recent violent storms have caused numerous breaches in banks of the Great Ouse. Vast fields remain flooded, left by their owners and occupiers, resulting in even scarcer tax receipts. There is a shortfall in the coffers to repay interest on old loans, let alone repay the capital, or to make essential repairs, and the only obvious solution is to borrow more money.

'We should sell more of the derelict estates,' says one.

'Who will buy land that stands underwater?' asks another, and the familiar chorus continues.

'Gentlemen, we need a different strategy,' Lord Townshend cuts in. 'We know the only permanent solution is to improve the outlet to sea, but we fought and were blemished by that battle ten years ago. We need a campaign that can be put into action before next winter. What I suggest, gentlemen, is that we find a way to force those who damage the banks to pay for their repair.'

An emphatic wave of agreement comes from the Board but some throw up their hands.

'What use is that when the traders won't pay the tolls?' they ask.

Lord Townshend walks over to a map of the Great Level set up on the wall of the meeting room and points to the district between the Cam, Ouse and Mildenhall rivers.

'Here, around Soham and down to Mildenhall, is where flooding is most severe and persistent. Barges already pay tolls along some stretches here where the banks are maintained by individual parishes. There is agreement to the principal of tolls in Parliament and little resistance on the ground, excepting as always, the Lynn merchants.

'We should apply for an amendment of the 1758 Act. That relates only to selling land in this particular area, but we should add a section on applying tolls on these rivers for upkeep just around here.' He waves his arm around Ely and bangs on the wall. 'If they don't pay, we'd have the power to seize barges and everything in them,' he says.

'There will be strong opposition from Cambridge,' some warn him.

'Most probably, but we must ensure they won't be heeded. We can do that, gentlemen?' He looks questioningly at those with connections in Parliament, who look at each other and nod. Then for the benefit of the others, he continues.

'Cambridge will be isolated. It's too far from Lynn for Lynn's arguments to be given much weight, and no other force is strong enough. What I'm proposing is a military style attack on all the opponents of tolls. Break that damn alliance here, and the rest may be so discomforted that they'll fall like skittles. It is a standard military tactic to divide multiple adversaries. Another is the element of surprise, and we should use both to our advantage.'

The Conservators lean back in their chairs. It seems a reasonable plan, but if it is argued out of Parliament it will be an expensive failure.

'We'd have to give the legal public notices, there's no getting around that.'

'Yes, yes, of course, but that's only three weekly newspaper publications and notices on church doors. Timing is all. The next session of Parliament will be early February. Public notices can be delayed till late December. If we maintain secrecy until then, have a perfect application, are ready with a complete, objection-free draft of the amendment,' he raises his eyebrows in question at the lawyers among them, 'and are quietly confident of no bureaucratic delays,' he looks again at the Ministers of Parliament, 'this could be passed by May. The critical element is to catch them unawares with an overwhelming advance. Then, while they're regrouping, we should plan our next move.'

Their petition is presented to Parliament in early February, and Royal Assent is given to this Ely Drainage Bill on 19th May 1789. Meanwhile, to address the Corporation's own debt, they start to actively pursue their most high profile non-payers of tax, to encourage payments from others.

Lord Townshend observes that they also need to know about the state of the Great Ouse by Lynn without delay, and suggests a survey of the river from Wiggenhall St. Germans to Lynn to provide the current dimensions and to recommend options.

Accordingly, they approach engineers Thomas Hyde Page and Robert Mylne. Neither is available, but in his place Hyde Page sends Thomas Cubit, his past associate at Woolwich Arsenal. Cubit works with John Watté, schoolteacher and astronomer of Leverington, near Wisbech, who has previously surveyed the Duke of Bedford's Fenland estates, and areas around the River Nene. Their own Mr. Golborne assists them, and their map is sent to Mylne for his attention.

Robert Mylne is a highly respected engineer. He has achieved a stellar reputation since he won a competition against many better known engineers to build a new bridge over London's Thames at Blackfriars in 1759. Then aged only twenty six, Blackfriars Bridge was his first major project. Since then, his classically designed buildings and bridges, in combination with close attention to costings and schedules have made his services highly sought after. He is also Surveyor for the New River Company which brings fresh water from Hertfordshire into London.

## King's Lynn
1789

*I carry the rowers who weave between towering ships to the Common Staithe. They draw in their oars and wipe sweat from their brows, for the sun has risen hot. One stays to clean bird droppings from the seats. The other calls for Golborne and Mylne, and they all go forth to measure my waters.*

*Yesterday I watched Mylne, striding my west bank as if it was his own, yammering all the while with his young son and Golborne. The older man's tongue is a precision tool that convinces doubters of his version of the unknowable, and wheedles the vain into prestige projects. He has bent many a water to his will and he intends to succeed with me where generations before him have failed. He is a troublesome man.*

*Today they go down deep channels to the outfall and the becalmed funnel of the open sea. Around them, the marsh belches its noisome flatulence in invisible clouds that waft to the estuary. Soon, Mylne will return to London with the odour of rotting eggs fixed firmly in his clothes.*

## Wiggenhall St. Germans
## October 1789

By October, landowners meeting at the Three Tuns in Wiggenhall St. Germans give notice of their intention to raise stiles on the banks to prevent haling altogether from the beginning of November if traders fail to pay more towards maintaining the banks.

The merchants are furious. The port will be at a standstill. Landowners have no right to set such conditions. What do they actually want?

By early December, the landowners have decided on the rate and conditions on which they will permit haling once more and they announce they will be at the Dukes Head, Lynn on 23rd December so that traders can sign an agreement to indicate their consent to the new demands.

In response, Alderman Thomas Bagge calls a meeting in Cambridge of all those interested in trade and navigation to discuss the landowners' conditions of higher tolls and restrictions on the manner of haling. Bagge has interests in both camps as his family own both merchant ships and an estate on the banks of the river at Tilney-cum-Islington. Men crowd into the meeting, anxious that their arguments be heard.

'Their demands are extortionate, far more than is needed to keep the banks in repair. We already pay a toll and that should be sufficient,' says one independent barge owner.

'More than that, it's not possible to hale a gang with only one horse with ropes fastened as they demand. A single animal does not have enough power, although we could try to manage with just two at most times,' another suggests.

Thomas Bagge puts to them that it is Parliament that should give them leave to hale on the banks under proper conditions, and decide what constitutes a fair cost, to which they agree. He directs that the committee of landowners be given a copy of their proceedings, before their meeting on 23rd December, and be told that the traders wish to settle the matter amicably. Payments made for many years past should continue while the application to Parliament is made.

The landowners judge that this does not offer a single suggestion, just delays and more delays. The traders might take a whole year over presenting their application to Parliament. They resolve to shortcut them and present their own petition. In the meantime, to keep up the pressure, they threaten to put stops on the banks from February.

By the first week in February, the merchants' petition is before Parliament, while the landowners trail by another two weeks. Neither progresses beyond the first committee stage. A joint Bill protecting both parties is adopted in Parliament, and passes as the Haling Act in May 1790.

It is a triumph for Parliamentary authority in preventing vigilante action from landowners or abuse by traders and ensures a fair apportionment of costs to both. All parties are content with its provisions and claim success for themselves that the Haling Act has achieved objectives beyond their initial expectations.

This rare taste of Parliamentary victory encourages Lord Townshend to consider further manoeuvres but he is called away by the King to raise corps of militia, to get them trained and ready to defend the country against an increasing threat from the French. Philip Yorke, 3rd Earl of Hardwicke at Wimpole, takes up the task of marshalling the lawyers and Parliamentary ministers of the Bedford Level Corporation.

## King's Lynn
## August 1790

> *I stand newly gorged. A parched summer depleted my freshwater and weakened me. I am become a feeble partner in a promenade to and fro with the tide, too thin to grind sands back to the ocean. The long summer thickens my bed which grows heavy until relentless rain returns. Now I thunder, my waters compete to overflow my shallow streams and I pour over their fields. There is no green, no gold, only my dirty brown waters.*

The summer meeting of the Marshland Commissioners of Sewers is growing raucous. With good reason, thinks their solicitor and secretary Robert Whincop, but it isn't his place to say so. The Commissioners of Sewers have authority to manage local drains. They are chaired by a Justice of the Peace, and by long standing custom on issues which affect the community such as drainage, the Commissioners sit with local farmers as jurors so that decisions are properly informed.

The Haling Act might reduce spending on the Great Ouse banks if a juror's land happens to be alongside the river, but it will not protect estates in central Marshland from flood. Persistent rain is adding to the already waterlogged condition of their crops. The harvest will be scarce again. There is a need to restore the grain supply, not to mention their soil to profit. Only the most prosperous Marshland proprietors have additional incomes besides their crops. The majority rent their farms and are sinking into financial ruin after successive poor years. Anxiety strains normal courtesies and an immoderate few thrash about looking for someone to blame. The Chairman cuts short their grumbling and directs them to the business in hand.

Mr. Whincop reads out a list of questions he has received from James Watt in answer to a new enquiry on the use of steam pumps to drain land. The previous meeting had heard from Mr. Evans, agent for Vice Admiral William Bentinck of Terrington St. Clement whose estate stretched for hundreds of acres along a coastal strip from the Nene to the Great Ouse. He reported that Bentinck's Dutch family owned Rhoon near Rotterdam, where a Boulter and Watt steam powered engine pump proved successful in 1782, and the Commissioners wanted to know if it could be replicated in Marshland.

'Mr. Watt asks what area is in need of drainage and how much rain falls on it in any one month. I told him forty thousand acres.'

'No, not that much, we're not draining all of Fenland.'

This starts a new debate. They add up what they reckon is the acreage of the relevant area and settle on about four thousand acres.

'How much rain?'

'Well, sometimes it's pouring on one field and not on another. Nobody measures it, so how can we say what it is?'

'We need to agree an average. Is it a foot a month or an inch?'

'No, not a foot.'

'Closer to two inches. Say one and a half.'

'What's the average each year?'

'Obviously, eighteen inches,' they confirm in unison.

'What quantity can be run off by the natural outfalls in

the worst seasons, and for what portions of the year can it be drained this way?'

'None! The present outfalls are silted up by sands in the river, and there never has been complete drainage in winter.'

'What is the height of high water above your land, and is that caused by land floods, inblowing of the wind or natural tides?

They grasp at the easy part and search for agreement on the first.

'Land flood and tides. Four, maybe five feet?' they suggest.

'It's been higher when there's a northwest blow. Six or seven I'd say.'

'Why does Mr. Watt ask?'

'I presume to enable him to calculate the amount of water that needs to be shifted in flood conditions.'

'In that case we'd better say eight feet.'

'That would mean a flood would be over the heads of every man here,' Whincop ventures.

'Nevertheless. Eight feet.'

Whincop writes 'Eight feet'.

'How many good outfalls and do they open to rivers or the sea?'

'Two outfalls into a large tidal river, but they are silted up for want of backwater for twelve months past.'

'How many windmills?'

'None.'

'Mr. Watt also asks for a scale map of the whole area.'

'There's only old maps. We have had no need. We all know our own lands.'

'I may have one,' Mr. Edwards offers.

'Mr. Whincop, will that suffice?' asks the Chairman who has noticed a restlessness and is keen to close the meeting before it erupts again. 'Make sure Watt sends you a cost estimate.'

'I'll see to it, sir.'

By October, Watt decides the replies given are not satisfactory for calculating a quote, and the Commissioners engage William Jessop, experienced from his Fenland work on the River Witham at Boston, to provide some answers. Jessop determines there are two ways of draining the area. The first is to cut a drain leading to a new outfall into the river below Lynn. The second is to use engines to raise water to the present outlet.

Jessop calculates the Marshland area to be 33,000 acres of which 21,000 is high enough to drain without mechanical assistance. This leaves 7,000 acres which are imperfectly drained as well as nearly 5,000 including Marshland Fen, Broad Fen and the Smeeth which are not drained at all and lie with three foot of water on them. Water from 7,000 acres needs to be raised by four feet and the rest by about eight feet into a new outlet.

Jessop agrees with Watt's conclusion that one large engine with two smaller engines will be needed to avoid one huge engine that would be unmanageable and under used during low rainfall.

The final quote for the large pump to raise water by eight feet is £1,290, plus a house for it. The two smaller pumps together are £2,700. In all they will consume four to six bushels of coal an hour, costing about five shillings a bushel. Additional fees of over £150 a year will be required until 1800 when the Boulton and Watt patent runs out.

The Marshland Sewer Commissioners calculate these costs against those of simply cutting a new drain across the area. The drain alone will be hard enough to finance in the face of the hardship being experienced by tenants and landowners, and nobody is entirely convinced how well it will work on its own.

Reports circulate that the Bedford Level Corporation are re-examining Kinderley's old proposals for a Cut at Wiggenhall St. Germans. In the face of the colossal cost of the steam engines, the Marshland Commissioners and jurors decide to wait, in the knowledge that if numerous men of philosophy and science believe a Cut would solve all their problems at once, they would use every means at their disposal to encourage all parties to agree on making something happen, quickly.

## The River Great Ouse
## January 1791

*I listen to murmurs from panelled offices and private parlours. They talk of old maps, then send their best men to measure me anew. They bore into my banks to see the grain of my ancient ground. They probe my water. I settle one day and move the next. I shift my shoals and confound them.*

*The old philosophers and the men of new science challenge each other. One is right, the other is wrong. They try to describe my being from numbers which forever change. They are each certain, and commit their contemplations to great machines which print their judgements for all to read. They claim independence, experience, honesty, but their only true agreement is with whoever pays them.*

*They blame my outfall for the mischief of their employer's neglect of my waters, but they cannot agree even on where my outfall is to be found. Some say it is the harbour. Some say the estuary, some say further away still.*

*I slither from them. I hide in opaque swirls. I engulf their pride like a primeval amoeba. They will not solve my mystery.*

## King's Lynn
## January 1791

A meeting of the Marshland Commissioners of Sewers is attended by Alderman John Cary of Eau Brink, and Sir Martin Browne Folkes, a newly elected MP for Lynn. Alderman Henry Bell of Wallingon Hall, a thousand acre estate upriver from

Wiggenhall who was the Mayor of King's Lynn Corporation in 1789, also attends. The meeting resolves that a Cut from the bend of the river to Lynn, as formerly proposed by Mr. Kinderley, would effect a proper outfall and at the same time improve navigation. They call for a general meeting to canvass opinions.

### The Crown and Anchor, Strand, London
### June 1791

Henry Bell chairs a meeting called to promote a new Bill through Parliament for authority to construct the Cut. They engage engineers James Golborne, John Smeaton and John Watté to calculate the costs of all the works required for a Cut in the style of Kinderley and instruct them to work separately, so the best range of opinion might be achieved. Smeaton declines, so Robert Mylne is approached again.

Watté's report judges the situation deplorable, with the water swirling from side to side in a serpentine manner around high shifting sands. There are eddies of fifteen to twenty feet deep and whirlpools of counter-currents that wear the banks severely and can take a boat onto the sands in minutes. The entire income of lands alongside some stretches is scarcely enough to cover the maintenance of their banks. The river bed at Denver Sluice is three feet higher with silt now than it was when Mr. Golborne the Elder made his observations in 1777 and it is worsening every year.

Watté's verdict is to make a new Kinderley style Cut to divert the Great Ouse into a straight narrow channel. This will lower water at Wiggenhall St. Germans Bridge by four foot six inches, an improvement that will be felt proportionately at the outfall of every drain throughout the South and Middle Levels. He also proposes a deep drain across Marshland to augment the force of the waters and improve its capacity to clear sands through to the outfall.

Golborne produces a lengthy analysis in August which also concludes that the Cut is essential and the single most effective means of improving the situation. More, he specifies the dimensions required and states his opinion that a greater force of water to clear sands and improve the outfall can be obtained from a deep drain across Marshland to join the river near Tilney, just before the proposed route of the Cut. He calculates it will cost £38,000.

Robert Mylne makes a third report using Watté's map, and agrees that a new Cut is essential.

These reports form the basis of a new petition to Parliament, but the petition stumbles twice because immediate objections are raised that adequate notice had not been placed in a couple of villages that are affected, and the petition has to be withdrawn.

## King's Lynn
## September 1791

King's Lynn Corporation recognises a growing threat to the harbour through silting and local agitation for the new Cut. It needs to be met with the best intelligence they can summon. John Smeaton's detailed report of the harbour in 1767 is out of date, and they commission Joseph Hodskinson, another experienced Fenland engineer, to give his opinion on the probable effect of the new Cut on the harbour.

Hodskinson is vehemently against the proposed new Cut. He observes that the present widening of the river above King's Lynn acts as a reservoir which moderates the force of the downstream current in the harbour. Without it, currents will be caused of such violence that ships could be ripped from their moorings. It is essential to maintain this safety valve, he says, especially as new navigations opening upstream increase the speed of fresh waters descending after storms.

He agrees the weaker force of waters from the reservoir needs to be concentrated in order to clear sands. He proposes a system of jetties in both the reservoir and the harbour to direct the flow into a narrower central course, which will offer clearance and safety. He reflects that Kinderley had discussed the potential benefits of a drain across Marshland to improve the outfall, but suggests it should meet the river as low down as possible, beyond the harbour.

His report is published in October. It prompts a wave of malicious pamphlets and anonymous comments in the press. In December he decides to re-publish, adding his response to the criticism, to preserve his reputation.

## Ely
### April 1792

The Bedford Level Corporation had set aside two days for landowners from across the region to have their say on the current ideas for a Kinderley style solution. Complainants flock to the meeting and outnumber those who might agree to the plan. In a majestic display of stalling, the Corporation decrees that no decisions can be made unless more owners from across the South and Middle Levels are able to give their opinion too.

The commissioners reserve their legal authority over the drainage but silently abdicate responsibility to the consent of local owners. Another meeting is scheduled for mid-May, in the town of March, over twenty miles away on rutted and dangerous carriageways.

This gives time for the tentacles of the Bedford Level Corporation to reach across the Level, into every mansion and church, and every local Court of Sewers. By the end of April, at the General Session of Sewers in King's Lynn, nineteen jurors resolve that the River Great Ouse between Wiggenhall St. Germans Bridge and Lynn is silted up and the works of sewers greatly impeded. They ask the Bedford Level Commissioners to take into their serious consideration such relief and assistance as should be thought proper. On the same day, twenty one jurors of the Court of Sewers of Clackclose, Downham Market, come to the same decision.

## March, Cambridgeshire
## May 1792

Fifty-seven people attend a meeting of independent landowners, chaired by the Earl of Hardwicke. He receives vigorous support from the twelve Reverend clerks attending. The Hon. Rev. Charles Lindsay, Vicar of Wisbech St. Peter and St. Paul is Hardwicke's brother-in-law; Rev. Joseph Plumptre of Newton in the Isle, near Wisbech is personal chaplain to Hardwicke's aunt at Wimpole, their family seat, and Rev. Thomas Sheepshanks, a Yorkshire man of considerable influence in Wisbech, is Plumptre's curate. Agents for the Deans of York and Litchfield, both with estates in the area, and Rev. Pemberton of Upwell join George Maxwell, a surveyor and agent for Lord Eardley, who is a Bailiff of the Bedford Level Corporation. Agents for several other Peers and their widows combine with twenty local landowners in an orchestrated choir of agreement.

They think Hodskinson's plan for King's Lynn Corporation is unlikely to render the drainage perfect, or the navigation certain and safe. The plan approved by Messers. Mylne, Golborne, Watté and others is more likely to lessen the expense of banks, mills and sewer works, thereby rendering the country perfect, and the navigation certain and safe. They reason that it is absolutely necessary to protect the country from destruction, and they will unite with all persons inclined to support the measure.

Navigators who use the river should co-operate in the improvement, they consider, since they will also derive advantages from it. They judge that £45,000 will be needed, which can be raised by a tax of four pence an acre for ten years.

Moreover, since the navigation will be safe, and expenses in tolls lessened, it is reasonable that barge owners should make some contribution to the works. The rate for tonnage laid on the navigation should be vested in Commissioners for Navigation for repairs and other works to improve the rivers and outfall through Lynn harbour.

All those present form an Eau Brink Committee in a new initiative to obtain an Act, and open a fund for expenses. They pledge all subscriptions will be re-paid out of the first money raised in taxes under the proposed Act.

As soon as the draft Act is published, the Earl of Hardwicke receives several appeals from the Haddenham area. They object to paying more tax to pay for a scheme which, they claim, will not benefit them in the least. Their fields are dry most of the time, except during winter storms when the Ouse overflows a little, but what they know of engineers' reports leads them to believe the depth of flood will be worse if the Cut goes ahead.

Mumblings of criticism circulate against Hardwicke which he counters by employing engineer John Hudson at his own expense to report on the proposals with respect to Haddenham and Littleport. Hudson reports that he too thinks the Cut would improve the depth of the outfall. He confirms the height of the river is unlikely to rise higher than at present, and recommends clearance work around the junction of the River Cam.

### The Crown and Anchor, Strand, London
### May 1792

At the end of May, the new Eau Brink Committee meets again. Robert Mylne explains the technicalities of the proposals using Watté's map as reference. Sir Martin Browne Folkes still prefers Hyde Page's earlier suggestion of embankment because it appears to be altogether less risky.

As well, he knows Mylne from ten years previously when he had given evidence on whether increased silting in Wells-next-the-Sea harbour was caused by an embankment across a creek built by Sir John Turner of Warham, Browne Folkes's late father-in-law. Mylne said that the same silting was happening all along that stretch of coast, irrespective of embankments. The verdict was in favour of Browne Folkes, but Mylne's arrogant attitude towards the court contributed to the harbour Commissioners appealing on the grounds that they had not known Mylne's evidence would be presented. At the second trial, Browne Folkes asked John Smeaton for an opinion. Smeaton agreed with Mylne, but had not actually surveyed the area. The court refused to admit his opinion saying it was only opinion and not based on facts as seen, and the verdict was for the Commissioners. Browne Folkes appealed to the Lord Chief Justice who ruled that where matters of skill or science are to be decided, the opinion of those peculiarly acquainted with it from their professions or pursuits may be admitted to assist juries, and the evidence must be presented to both parties before a trial. He ordered a third trial to include Smeaton's opinion.

Although Browne Folkes, as a lawyer, was gratified that his perseverance had contributed to the future acceptance of expert witness opinion in court, it had involved long and costly legal wrangling on his own behalf which might have been prevented if Mylne had approached the court more constructively in the first place.

Today, Mylne's explanations to the Eau Brink Committee are incomplete. His responses to questions are confusing and some are glossed over altogether. Browne Folkes fears something similar to his own experience is afoot now, and he'll be damned if he'll allow Mylne to foul these proceedings as well. He suggests the meeting adjourns to consider the answers Mylne has given, and to reconvene the next day to permit further enquiries. Mylne says he has to attend a Bedford Level Corporation meeting the next day, so they agree he will return at an early hour for a short session.

That evening, over dinner with wine and brandy, conversation wanders to more extravagant demands. 'Why isn't there a bridge at Lynn? It is ridiculous to have to use a ferry when the opposite bank is so close. It's either that, or a tedious twelve mile trudge via Wiggenhall bridge, just to reach further afield. Surely a bridge would allow a direct road link to the River Nene, and with a bridge over that too, a shorter journey by miles to Lincolnshire?'

'But it's a very wide river,' companions reply. 'There would have to be several supports immersed in the waterway and

Lynn is sure to complain that the obstruction will hasten silting.'

'Nonsense. Long spanned bridges are being built all over the place and they don't cause problems. Ask Mylne tomorrow. He's worked on some himself. Anyway, isn't the point of this whole debate to eliminate silting?'

Next morning, a few heavy-eyed landowners straggle in to be faced with Mylne in peak form. Browne Folkes reflects that yet again, Mylne has calculated his audience accurately. Those attending this morning might hear any explanation, and they'd be convinced into general approval. With this, Mylne hurries off to Lynn to calculate where posts should be placed to mark the mid-line of the New Cut. He smiles to himself. Another fine bridge would be a pleasing contribution to his professional work.

## Marshland
## September 1792

*I glide beneath an autumn mist that hangs in a thin cloud at arms-length above the fields. Already a kindly sun strengthens. Soon the air will clear and the weather promises a truce; neither the steaming humidity of summer nor the deluge of recent winters.*

The Reverend Joseph Plumptre and his curate Thomas Sheepshanks of St. James Church, Newton in the Isle, start out for a meeting at the Rose and Crown in Wisbech. They hope to have avoided excesses of vitriol between opposing sides by advertising the meeting as one for landowners and others 'who were inclined to concur in the intended application to Parliament for the Cut from Eau Brink to Lynn'. Inflammatory remarks could destroy what they hope will be a constructive contribution to the resolution of the drainage question with respect to the drain across Marshland.

Rev. Plumptre opens the meeting by reading letters from three of Marshland's major landowners, including Vice Admiral

William Bentinck, which support the general proposals for the Cut. Their views will be influential. Then Rev. Sheepshanks summarises the engineers' reports, including works to dig a new drain in Marshland.

'Have any of them said exactly where this Marshland drain will run?' one asks.

'They all have different opinions. Where it should run or fall out to the Ouse or even whether it is needed, who's to know?'

They look at each other, hoping someone will supply an answer.

'I'm against agreeing to any scheme without the course being set out so we can make our own determination,' a man from Wisbech speaks up, expecting agreement from the meeting.

'The esteemed gentleman is right. It's impossible for us to judge. We should know the significance of all the reports, before we agree to any scheme.' Heads nod around the room.

'We should get an engineer's impartial view of the proposals as they affect Marshland,' Sheepshanks suggests. 'Perhaps ask Mr. Rennie or Mr. Hudson? At any rate someone with Fenland experience who has not been consulted before.'

By February 1793, a report from John Rennie is in their hands. It is short, simple and clear. Nothing done in Marshland will improve drainage unless the outfall of the Great Ouse is improved. A Cut at Eau Brink would significantly improve the scouring effect of the river and clear the outfall. This would not only improve drainage throughout the river system and restore the harbour but make it deep enough for larger ships to use. He recommends jetties at West Lynn to concentrate the ebb flow further into the bay to clear a safer approach to the harbour. These works would permit effective draining of all but the lowest lying parts of Marshland, for which he recommends a steam engine to speed water into existing drains but he repeats that a single engine alone would be ineffective without an improved outfall.

**King's Lynn**
**April 1793**

*I vibrate with the hammerings of war. Men feed coal to glowing furnace shells, and melt grey stones till they run like the spirit of the earth itself. They fashion all manner of tools to harm their enemies on land and sea.*

*Men risk life to protect their kin. They trail like giant ravenous worms across foreign lands and converge in orgies of destruction and killing. Their heads survive to grow new bodies which march in a different direction. But to me, men who use soft words to gain their ends are more dangerous. When the carnage subsides, these men will return to condemn me with hot embers still aglow in their hearts.*

Maxey Allen, veteran Mayor of Lynn, gathers the Councillors of the town to receive yet another report they have commissioned, this from engineer Joseph Nickalls. They are anxious, as always, about the integrity of the harbour and commerce of the town, but more so now that their veto on dangerous proposals seems to be fading.

Nickalls had inspected the main waterways to Lynn and down to the Crutch of the estuary. He found a vast expanse of stagnated water around Ely, and at Denver Sluice there was a scene of inundation which presented the most painful sensation to him. He found mills which were built and maintained at great expense as defective as the state of the river itself, and watergates that were unable to open even in a wind with the strength of four horses. The shifting sands were perpetually variable and impossible to render stationary by human art or contrivance.

From his borings along the line of the proposed Cut, he deduced that there was no substance that could be considered suitable as a base for embankments, and more, that so much water would seep into the workings that it would be impractical to pump out enough to excavate the bottom of the Cut.

He took issue with details in the reports from most other engineers and suggested the river should be restored to its state in 1758 after rebuilding Denver Sluice. He thought if the river were straightened upriver from Knights Goole, a drain near Tilney, then the new Cut would not be necessary. He didn't have the gift of prophesy, he said, but if the new Cut ever takes place, it will be the ruin of drainage and annihilation of Lynn harbour.

'Gentlemen,' Mayor Allen concludes, 'I'm sure you join me in recognising the devastation Nickalls has described, but I had hoped he would suggest more realistic alternatives. Telling us the harbour will be ruined, even if he does give detailed contradiction of other reports, gets us no closer to a reasoned argument against the Cut. It's his opinion versus that of many others.'

Alderman Elsden replies. 'It's obvious to everyone that we have to prevent the harbour silting up, or the port cannot function. The need is urgent. We have to find a way to manage this in which we can be reasonably confident of a minimum of hurt to all parties.'

'The local men who promote this Bill are a disgrace to society,' another declares. 'They preach their fairness in calling for just ten years of land tax, while encumbering traders with the maintenance costs of the entire drainage for ever. Where is the minimum of hurt in that? What funds will be left when they get their money back? And they want us to pay for their lawyers as well?'

'It is being formulated with scant attention to Lynn's needs,' Alderman Everard judges and then turns to Maxey Allen.

'Mr. Mayor, the meetings I have attended on this subject have been beset by a rabble of vulgar men. It is impossible to ascertain facts in the tumult. Reasoned argument is interrupted and belittled. There is aggression and aggrandisement in equal measure, but no negotiation. It will ever be so if matters remain in the hands of the present Eau Brink Committee, and that way lies ruin for us all. Our concerns are invisible in the drafts of the proposed Bill. I'd be more likely to consider a plan contrived by a more representative group than that leading proceedings now.'

Henry Bell offers a diplomatic proposal, concerned that he might be viewed as a turncoat, a trusted local man now seen to be promoting the Bill. Yet he is as keen as any to reduce flooding on his estate.

'I suggest that a new body be formed, with fewer, but more representative men, delegated from all areas that will be affected by this Parliamentary business. It could be, for example, two each from the Middle and South Levels, Marshland, the town and harbour and lastly the inland countries and navigation. Ten in all. They should be gentlemen who can, if necessary, hold their positions but be able to recognise when to compromise. This body should be charged with the responsibility of coming up with a plan, and be able to direct engineers without bias. We, then, must undertake to work with and agree with whatever they decide.'

Maxey Allen pauses. Bell's opinion could be a solution of sorts, but he does not have the long years of experience in managing river affairs that's shared by most of the Councillors. It has a whiff of revolution about it. Was it right to renounce old obligations with such ease? Over the years, King's Lynn Corporation had wrestled many times with the navigation issue and always, the conflicts diverted them from constructive action.

By a 1619 charter from King James I, King's Lynn Corporation had exercised full Admiralty powers on shipping from the bridge at Wiggenhall St. Germans to Blakeney Haven for which the Corporation was responsible to no-one but the King. This included the Corporation holding its own Admiralty Court for policing and collection of customs which enabled more control over the previously corrupt Admiralty officials, but their obligation weighed more heavily now the river's channels were clogging so badly.

Now, a bucket of water drawn from the haven is half full of sand when left to stand. If only a fraction of this remains after each ebb, it explains why the river is increasingly shallow especially after a dry summer when rain water draining from the higher ground dwindles. An unfriendly wind could force more of their ships onto the shoals, and this would be compounded if a Lynn trader tries to use a larger ship as were being handled elsewhere. They are losing out to competition in larger ports.

Allen feels a personal obligation as well, to hand on a functioning port business to the next generation, just as he had received it from four generations of his family. His own son is now a Common Councillor on the Corporation. Many of the heirs of past generations of merchants such as the Everards and Bagges who sat around the table today are his extended family through blood, marriage or inheritance, from which all their businesses had benefitted. So too, the vast majority of the townspeople, and many beyond, who flourished on its river trade.

His instinctive reluctance to grasp Bell's suggestion is not only about old family honour, but more nostalgia for times when life seemed more predictable, more controllable. The haven, the world even, is different now. The revolutionary movements against rightful Kings at home and abroad destabilise trading and put their ships in danger. First the Americans, then the French and the Irish, even men here in Lynn complain that they want representation in the governance of their situations. All the same, Lynn had prospered under the Corporation's management. What would the mass decide given the Corporation's present dilemma? Allen wonders.

As for joining up as equals in a new body? It was naive. It would not take long for the Bedford Level Corporation and the landed gentry to infiltrate and dominate proceedings. The evidence was Bell himself. He was certainly not a merchant. He and his family were major local landowners.

Still, Allen can't recall a time when silting in the river had caused such problems before.

There seemed no way out. Do nothing and the port will be ruined. Of the remedies offered, one may fail, the other may destroy what they aimed to protect. Engineers had failed to help them decide.

Across the table he catches John Cary's gaze and a sad shake of his head. He's bound by the old ways too but has no answer to offer now, except that it should not be their responsibility alone.

'What is the view of you all on this?'

'It has to be an improvement on our present situation,' the majority reply comes, with conviction.

'Very well then. Are there three Councillors who will discuss this with Sir Martin Browne Folkes? And if he agrees, ask him to take this to the highest authority without delay.'

By mid-April, the Gentlemen of Lynn have delivered their proposal to Charles Yorke, MP for Cambridgeshire and half-brother of Philip, 3rd Earl of Hardwicke. Charles Yorke replies that Hardwicke intends to bring the proposal to a meeting of the Eau Brink Committee in June at Cambridge, and suggests that all parties might meet then on fair and amicable terms.

When the day comes, the Gentlemen of Lynn depute four of their body to act on their behalf. Hardwicke had forwarded the proposal, but is unable to attend the meeting.

Undaunted, the Lynn party send Mr. Forster, their secretary, to inform William Walcot who is chairing that day's meeting of the Eau Brink Committee, that they are willing to attend on the Committee if so desired. By midday, their idea is under consideration and the Lynn party are waiting for an invitation to explain it in more detail.

In due course, Mr. Forster appears to tell them that the Committee especially convened to conduct the Bill through Parliament have decided that they have no powers to receive any proposal other than one that might simply amend a clause in the present Bill.

Disappointed, but still keen to preserve the benefit of their intentions, the Lynn party invite the Eau Brink Committee to join them in calling for a public meeting to consider their initiative proposal for joint working.

Several hours later, William Walcot sends their decision. He confirms that the Eau Brink Committee meeting that day are not authorised to agree to any proposal which differs from the principles of the Bill for the new Cut. They will consider any new plan for better drainage and navigation which is calculated to produce a union between proposers and opposers, but the Lynn proposal did not include alternative details on the Cut's construction, and until they receive such a plan, the Committee think it unnecessary to assemble the interested parties.

'Have the Committee even read the proposal we sent to the Earl of Hardwicke?' the Lynn men demand of Mr. Forster. 'Take them a copy of it and tell them that as they don't appear to have paid any attention to it, we ask again for their opinion, particularly regarding the benefit it offers for co-operation, and if, then, whether they don't think people of the area are entitled to give their sentiments on it.'

After more hours of difficult discussion, William Walcot sends his final decision. He knows it will incense the Lynn men, but he cannot convince the Eau Brink Committee that the Lynn offer is not simply a device to delay decisions still further.

Walcot does not command respect and discipline as Hardwicke would, but neither Hardwicke nor Charles Yorke have come to the meeting. Walcot dithers and finds chairing any meeting is purgatory. This should have been a routine meeting, a check of finance and recording of minor works for amendments to the Bill. Instead he faces this explosion of diabolical conflict.

How will he face the Lynn men if he meets them in the street? The men on this Committee might be right, legally speaking, but they did not live in Marshland. They were closeted in London or Cambridge, rarely even visiting their lands. Walcot determines there and then to leave the estate in Walsoken that was his father's legacy, to concentrate his interests in the family estate at Oundle, Northants, and leave them all to their arguments. For today though, the Committee is resolute. No plan has been offered that was likely to bring the business to a speedy and amicable conclusion, or which made it proper to call a public meeting.

The anger felt by the Gentlemen of Lynn by this rejection hardens over the summer. In August they take their argument to the newspapers, giving details of the events and the refusal of their offer. They invite the public to judge for themselves.

Does the Eau Brink Committee's work to promote the current Bill intend to put an end to the mischievous and expensive contest that divides the country?

Does the current Bill intend to unite all parties?

Does it secure equal justice to all in raising the expenses of the works?

And has the proposal of joint working made by the Gentlemen of Lynn been considered with due attention, or valued as worth putting to the public to decide?

Many will think not, the Lynn men predict.

The Gentlemen of Lynn declare they will remain ready to attend any meeting called for the purpose. They are sincerely disposed to promoting the improvement of the country, but they will firmly resist, to the utmost in their power, the partial and ill-conceived project which is being forced upon them. They are convinced that it is fraught with consequences of the highest degree injurious to drainage, navigation and private property.

And, they add, the proposed method of raising the funds is glaringly unequal, oppressive and unjust.

## London
## 1794

Sir Martin Browne Folkes is worried at the number of petitioners presenting in favour of the Cut. They have varied and sophisticated arguments, with proof of their financial losses through flood which are readily understandable by the Commons committee charged with analysing the evidence.

Those against the Cut are either unwilling to pay extra taxes on land they claim does not need draining, or they are simply fearful of a future catastrophe in the harbour. They have no practical alternative to offer, only the gut instinct of men who breathe salt air every day and have a deep respect for the power of the river to take life at will.

John Cary and his neighbours at least have produced a logical petition against it. Their lands close to Eau Brink will be cut off, sandwiched between the proposed route of the Cut and the old bank of the Ouse. Together the families installed drainage which is adequate most of the time. If the Cut goes ahead, they will be unable to get onto their fields because the road they constructed and maintained for decades will be fractured. Their fresh water supply will be cut off, so no animals can be kept, and they will have to leave their houses. Browne Folkes is disappointed that so few of the other opposers state their cases so clearly.

At the hearings at the end of March, the proponents of the Bill use every tactic they can devise to advance their cause. They call Sir Thomas Hyde Page to give evidence, ostensibly for fair play since they had started their evidence with Robert Mylne's opinion, but they have dragged Hyde Page from his sick bed and his voice is so weak that he has an assistant repeat his answers to make them audible. This involves a delay which requires a degree of patience on the part of the committee, and they are already frustrated with the entire issue.

Counsel makes much of changes that may have taken place in the passage of twenty years since Hyde Page had taken his view of the river at Lynn. Although it is far removed from a powerful presentation, Hyde Page sticks to his opinion. Embankment is the quicker, cheaper, safer option and should be tried first. He repeats that if the Cut is insisted upon, its dimensions will be critical.

The 1794 Parliamentary session grinds on to summer and arguments are still poles apart. The Commons committee seem unconcerned about safety, as long as a decision is made. The project has taken so long to reach this point that an extra few weeks needed for the Cut, compared to embankments, seems neither here nor there. Browne Folkes realises that if a strong argument is to be made against the Cut, it will be on the financial grounds of embankments being much less expensive.

**The River Great Ouse**
**Spring 1794**

> *I recognise the Redcoat's man, grown stouter now.*
> *His soldier's bearing is stiffer, but he holds his chin*
> *high into the wind. A man at ease with the seasons.*
> *He stops where my banks are broken down. He*
> *measures and prods, and his man and a boy scratch*
> *into a book before they pass along.*

Martin Browne Folkes writes to Hyde Page who sends Thomas Cubit to inspect and measure the banks on each side of the Great Ouse between Clayhithe and Lynn. Cubit reckons eighty-two miles of banking needs to be replaced or improved, and each side of the river from Denver to Lynn needs to be properly secured with fascines. Adding in the costs of superintendence and contingencies, Cubit estimates the whole works can be achieved for £1,000 pounds a mile or £82,000 in total.

Hyde Page visits Lynn when Cubit finishes his report. He examines the ground on which embankments might be built, and inspects the outfall. He finds it more deteriorated than he imagined, with a potential for impairing the efficiency of any moderate plan.

Even supposing James Golborne's estimate of around £38,000 for the whole Cut is low, or if some other work is found to be required which increases that estimate, Hyde Page cannot significantly close the gap between the two figures. Every engineer who recommends the Cut, rather than embankment, has implied much lower costs.

Browne Folkes will have to find another strategy before Parliament gathers for the next session on 30th December 1794. A way must be found to tackle silting in the outfall, or the harbour will inevitably decline. Lynn must tame its violent river and turn it to its advantage, or die.

## The River Great Ouse
## Summer 1794

*I am uncommonly still, slack now for tide upon tide, relaxed by drought upland.*

*The sun rises high. A horse rider comes close by. His journey has hours to run, miles along my banks to the rickety bridge at Wiggenhall before he can cross. He looks across my slim waters, spangled with reflections of high clouds and shields his eyes from my dazzle.*

*Horse and man drink from a trough by the bank. Refreshed, the rider wipes his brow and turns his mount into my waters. The horse hesitates at the unusual command, but he goes forward. His hooves tickle my sands, splashing from shoal to shoal to reach the opposite bank. Small fountains spring up around his step and fall back in a shower of sparkling iridescence. I am radiant.*

*The tide returns and I gather on the sandbanks. Men rouse themselves and their barges float through my channels once more.*

## King's Lynn
## October 1794

The Council assemble under their new Mayor, Edmund Rolfe Elsden. He had hoped for a calmer atmosphere for his first Mayoral chairmanship, but the grounding of a ship in the estuary that same week refocuses minds on the jeopardy to shipping presented by their rapidly silting haven. They are still smarting from the rejection of their recent proposal. This could be enough to keep Councillors ranting all day. Today though, he has to report on his meeting with Sir Martin Browne Folkes, and somehow manage to resuscitate a common approach to a solution for the silting problem.

'Gentlemen, the nation is called upon to mobilise for war in Europe. Several bodies of militia are planned across Norfolk and a number of us have been appointed to lead and train them, including Mr. Everard and myself.'

'Good men!' the Councillors interrupt, banging energetically on the table.

'My point is, gentlemen, that if our businesses are to thrive, if we are to manage the haven as well as doing our patriotic duty, we need to bring our commercial experience to this problem. We are all annoyed by the rebuff we have suffered, but the incentive is ours. We need to persist, just as we would if we want a new contract. We'd refuse to take no for an answer. Every one of us would compromise to get what we want.'

There are fewer plaudits now for Edmund Rolfe Elsden's views. They are certainly not the views his late father would have held in his long years of service on the Corporation. His father and grandfathers, all substantial merchants in Lynn, never compromised in business or their resolve to maintain the port.

John Cary is desperately worn out by the argument. It seems to have been going on all his life. He's been having nightmares of being buried alive, and takes this as an omen. He has set out detailed instructions in his Will in case he is consigned to his grave by an incompetent physic, and regaining consciousness, be unable to rise due to a slab of granite respectfully marking his place of rest. But in his dreams he is not resting. He is suffocating, willing the water to come to finish him off in a compassionate manner, but, for spite, it does not come and he is doomed to suffocate for ever. Now, he almost wants to quit the farm, but a residual daytime instinct tells him to hang on. He has generated a petition to Parliament in concert with his neighbour, Mr. Lane, to preserve his family lands, but there was no knowing if it would be effective. They planned to at least extract decent compensation if their lands were split such that they became uneconomic

Many Councillors now find themselves following more diverse business interests. Still, their newly acquired estates are as liable to flood as anyone else's and they want an end to the uncertainty of the port's future.

The Mayor's strongest ally is Alderman Henry Bell of Wallington Hall. He's made no secret of his enthusiasm for the Eau Brink Committee of which he has been a part since its first meeting in 1791. They are at last doing something that neither the King's Lynn nor the Bedford Level Corporations had seemed able to achieve for decades.

'Mr. Mayor,' Bell said, 'we have paid a fortune in attempts to obtain the best engineering advice available to guide our actions. Each report leaves us less certain and less able to determine what our decisions should be.

'We need to pin down engineers from both sides and make them agree on a way forward. I propose we approach the Eau Brink Committee with just such a proposal, and this time I will ensure the Corporation's proposal is properly respected. We should deputise a small number to represent us, and ask them to do the same. The fewer people to dissent in the room the better.

'We should state our sincere intent to create a new Bill between us, based on the advice agreed between the engineers from both sides, and that we intend that it will pass through Parliament in the next session,' Bell suggests.

'That leaves us open to accepting anything the engineers devise, whether or not we agree with it,' Rolfe Elsden objects.

'Well, what do we want?' Bell demands, exasperated. 'Decide that and add it to the proposal. Tell the Eau Brink Committee our preference and we can work jointly from there. The choices seem to be construct the Cut, create embankments or some other measure to contain waters between Wiggenhall and Lynn. But whatever is decided, we must agree to accept it, just as we resolved we would in the Spring.'

The whole congregation shift in their chairs. Bell is probably right, but it is uncomfortable to be reminded in such a challenging manner.

'There's another ship blocking the approach to the harbour and its cargo lost. More will follow if we do not act now,' Bell continues. 'We cannot indulge ourselves with this indecision any longer.'

'What about fascines?' John Cary suggests quietly. 'Hyde Page put a deal of faith in them when he was here.'

'We know the outfall is much more silted now. If Hyde Page is to be one of the engineers, he'd do well to inspect the outfall and the upper river now, to validate his opinion,' Bell replies.

The discussion begins to wander. Rolfe Elsden jumps in.

'Councillors, we need to agree. Is our proposal that we delegate a couple of our body to meet with a couple of the Eau Brink Committee, for us both to be able to call on engineers nominated from both sides with instructions to decide a way forward, based on reducing the spread of waters around Eau Brink?'

'Agreed, Mr. Mayor.'

'And that our aim is for the next Parliamentary session, so it should be agreed before January,' Bell adds.

'Quite so. Then that's our resolution. Alderman Bell, please make sure it progresses with the respect our intentions deserve. I'm sure you'll find a way.'

## The White Hart Inn, Newmarket
## Saturday, 27th December 1794

Henry Bell and his distant cousin Richard Greaves Townley of Fulborne, who has inherited the Beaupre Bell ancestral estate at Outwell, near Wisbech, join the Earl of Hardwicke and George Maxwell, agent for Lord Eardley, at the White Hart Inn. Townley is a Conservator of the Bedford Level Corporation, and has just ended a stint as Sheriff of Cambridgeshire. With their solicitor Edmund Saffery of Downham Market, they compose the delegates of the Eau Brink Committee.

Mayor Edmund Rolfe Elsden meets Thomas Bagge and Sir Martin Browne Folkes and they are joined by the Honourable Horace Walpole, the second of King's Lynn's two Ministers of Parliament. Also at the meeting are three recently elected Common Councillors for King's Lynn Corporation and their solicitor John Forster.

The Earl of Hardwicke takes the Chair and asks Browne Folkes to outline the report on embanking that Hyde Page had given him in the summer. This leads neatly to the proposition that the two engineers, Robert Mylne and Thomas Hyde Page, should meet as soon as possible and agree on a plan. As soon as this is received by the Earl of Hardwicke and the Mayor of Lynn, five gentlemen from each side should meet to attend to outstanding matters.

Mayor Rolfe Elsden glances around at his party who each nod their consent.

'If Hyde Page and Mylne can agree, so will we. On this condition, let the principle of the new Bill go ahead. We must all depend on both of them to bring the best of their combined experience to the issue. We can do no more.'

'Might we say the Bill can progress without need for more evidence to be given?' Henry Bell asks.

Rolfe Elsden looks round again and confirms agreement. Then they devise a common statement for their respective official records.

When the new session of Parliament opens on the following Tuesday, 30th December 1794, news spreads that King's Lynn Corporation will drop its opposition to the Eau Brink Cut, providing Mylne and Hyde Page can agree on the design and specifications of the work needed.

During January, work continues in Parliament on the various other related petitions, and between Mylne and Hyde Page. Charles Yorke presents the draft of the new Bill which is read the first time on 14th January 1795, and given its second reading on 4th February. Clauses describing its technical details will be added when agreed by the engineers and King's Lynn Corporation.

The engineers continue to work in close detail to lay down precise distances between the banks at various points along its length, and the angles of its sides in order to achieve maximum scour with the minimum of violent currents. Upriver, work on numerous sluices is described. The entire length of the river from Erith to Lynn is to be cleared of obstructions and deepened. The position of the Marshland Drain is determined as joining the Great Ouse at the upper end of the Cut by Wiggenhall. The proposed Act also requires the construction of a toll-free bridge at the curve of the Cut as it enters the harbour.

In early March, Mylne attends the Commons Committee where he reads out an agreement between himself and Hyde Page regarding the engineering aspects of the Cut, including the dimensions they have agreed on.

## King's Lynn
## 27th March 1795

At the next meeting of the King's Lynn Corporation, Mayor Edmund Rolfe Elsden presents a joint report from Thomas Hyde Page and Robert Mylne which states exactly the dimensions along the path of the Cut, its curves, its foreland banks and its internal slopes. It widens gradually from 370 feet at Wiggenhall St. Germans to the narrowest part of the harbour which is

278 yards (834 feet) by Ferry Staithe. Hyde Page and Mylne undertake to personally stake out the stated dimensions, and any other engineering issues are to be agreed by both of the engineers.

The Councillors of the Corporation accept the report, and drop their opposition to the Bill. By mid-April, the engineers' joint work on the plan allows the technical clauses in the Bill to be completed. The third reading of the Bill is passed in the Commons, approved by the House of Lords, and receives Royal Assent by the end of May 1795.

The Eau Brink Act of 19th May 1795 provides an Act of Parliament authorising improvement of the drainage of the Middle and South Levels, part of the Great Level of the Fens called Bedford Level, and the Low lands adjoining or near to the River Ouse in the county of Norfolk, draining through the same to the sea by the Harbour of King's Lynn and the said county; and for altering and improving the Navigation of the said River Ouse from or near a place called Eau Brink, in the parish of Wiggenhall St. Mary, in the said county to the said Harbour of King's Lynn and for improving and preserving the Navigation of the several rivers communicating with the said River Ouse.

The main provisions of the Act are that it authorises the construction of the Eau Brink Cut and specifies its dimensions but allows for these to be changed if found to be necessary and if agreed by both engineers. It requires the construction of a bridge across the River Great Ouse, and access roads from it to the wider area, outlines the amounts of land taxes and navigation tolls payable, and preserves the customary rights of King's Lynn Corporation and the Bedford Level Corporation over the River Great Ouse. It protects the lands of John Cary, Joseph Lane and Sir Martin Browne Folkes, and names those entitled to be Commissioners for Drainage and Commissioners for Navigation, both charged with the responsibility of carrying out their respective duties to build it, with due regard for the drainage issues throughout and navigation on the River Great

Ouse. Their work is separate from the existing Commissioners of Sewers, who are directed not to intermeddle in the affairs of the Eau Brink Commissioners.

Under the Eau Brink Act, to be eligible as a Commissioner for Drainage, persons are to own more than 200 acres, or be a Rector or Vicar of a parish in the area, or be the Mayor of Lynn.

Commissioners for Navigation are to have a personal estate of £1,000, or one worth the yearly value of £50. Those possessing land in the area who are Honourable servants of the Monarch holding senior public office or who are Knights of the Realm are eligible, as are the Burgesses and officers of the towns of Bury St. Edmunds, King's Lynn, Cambridge and Thetford, as well as the Vice Chancellor of Cambridge University and the Conservators of the River Cam. There are seventy eight named owners of smaller lands, eleven Reverend Clerks, 142 interested parties such as merchants and traders, and the Commissioners of Private Navigations such as those on the River Lark. Each Commissioner must take an Oath to confirm their eligibility and honourable behaviour. Meetings of each set of Commissioners are held separately but commonly occur at the same venue on the same day. Together their activities are here described as those of the Eau Brink Commissioners.

# The Eau Brink Commissioners

Sir Martin Browne Folkes
(21 May 1749 – 11 Dec 1821)

Vice Admiral William Bentinck
(17 June 1764 – 21 Feb 1813)

Sir Andrew Snape Hamond
(17 Dec 1738 – 12 Sept 1828)

# The Engineers

Sir Thomas Hyde Page
(1746 - 30 June 1821)

John Rennie
(7 June 1761 – 4 Oct 1821)

Robert Mylne
(4 Jan 1733 – 5 May 1811)

# Part Three
# The Vexing

# Part Three
# The Vexing


## The River Great Ouse
## 1795

*I am dismayed. Those who threaten me have ceased their ancient argument. United, both now turn on me; victorious, focussed, determined. They will find me a greater challenge than they dare to dread. I will see them all rot in their precious ground. I will ruin them.*


## The Duke's Head, King's Lynn
## 4th June 1795

The Eau Brink Commissioners meet for the first time at the Duke's Head, King's Lynn. Edmund Rolfe Elsden with fellow Aldermen of King's Lynn Corporation John Cary, and the brewing brothers Thomas and William Bagge, join farmers and landowners from close by. The meeting is chaired by Henry Bell's neighbour Thomas Berners Plestow of Watlington Hall, supported by Thomas Hare of Stowe. The sole member of the Bedford Level Corporation to attend is Thomas Ground of Whittlesea, past Sheriff of Cambridgeshire and Huntingdonshire.

They appoint William Lemmon, solicitor of Downham Market, as their Clerk, who notes the names of those present who each declare their oaths. They nominate auditors for the expenses of obtaining the Eau Brink Act and any person having such demands on the Commissioners is to deliver their accounts to Mr. Lemmon. The Commissioners instruct Thomas Hyde Page and Robert Mylne to proceed with their work.

## The White Hart Inn, March
## 9th July 1795

With the Parliamentary session now paused until August, the Earl of Hardwicke joins Henry Bell, Richard Greaves Townley, Thomas Ground, Thomas Berners Plestow and Gilbert Parke, the Vicar of Wiggenhall St Mary Magdalen, along with numerous other Eau Brink Commissioners. They confirm Richard Greaves Townley as a joint auditor for the expenses so far, and appoint bankers Gurney and Birkbeck as ongoing Treasurer. James Golborne and John Watté are to be Surveyors to execute works under the Act, and they are instructed to meet with Thomas Hyde Page and Robert Mylne when they set out the line. Commissioners are to make a return of the taxable land in their districts, and they declare a reduced offer for anyone wishing to pay the next ten years' tax in advance.

## London
## August 1795

In August, Sir Martin Browne Folkes tells the Eau Brink Commissioners that Hyde Page has told him he will not proceed further until the large map on which the approved line is drawn is deposited with Mr. Lemmon at Downham Market. They instruct Mr. Lemmon to request it from Mylne, and if he fails to send it, to visit him and collect it.

The Commissioners appoint surveyors to draw an accurate map of the affected area, noting the owners and extent of their land, so that their taxes can be assessed. The first year's collection of taxes is swallowed up in payments of substantial expenses to the promoters of the Bill, and colossal fees to their lawyers. For the next few years, the activity of the Eau Brink Commissioners is dominated by the collection of taxes. The tax collectors have such trouble extracting monies from those liable to pay that the Commissioners are forced to make an example of notable defaulters by issuing Warrants of Distress. Failure to pay will result in the removal of goods to the same value as their unpaid tax.

Increasingly, their meetings are inquorate. Attention is turning to Britain's response to the constantly changing military and naval campaigns of the French Revolutionary forces across Europe, led by a former Artillery Officer named Napoleon Bonaparte whose declared ambition is to invade Britain.

In December 1796 a landing in Ireland's Bantry Bay by French forces is foiled by storms and the British Navy. A landing at Fishguard in February 1797 results in surrender within two days, and another attempt in Ireland, at County Mayo in August 1797, assisted again by Irish revolutionary forces, is defeated in twelve days. These events bring the cold reality of an attack on mainland Britain much closer. Napoleon Bonaparte's armies are laying the countries of Europe before them, either by their victorious armies or peace treaty. Soon, Britain stands alone.

## King's Lynn
**1797**

*I smell the men who come with the stench of sweat and defeat. They stagger from the bowels of transport ships into barges which take them day after day still further into my gloomy mist.*

*What hell is this, they sob, where the barges fore and aft dissolve into a white fog?*

*What cursed country is this that has stunted trees growing out of the shallow sea like wraiths?*

*What damnation awaits us if we step out to escape this floating coffin?*

*Here there is no sound but a clamour within their own minds to survive. They long to touch solid ground, to hear the sharp call of a bird instead of the never-ending slurp, sucking just inches from them. These men do not flourish in water like my fish. The cold damp on their skins drags strength from them. They are living spectres.*

*I do not tell them their enemy has built huts to exclude them from the crash of war or that their capture saves them from the belligerent desires of men who care not if they live or die. They do not know that some will prosper in their confinement, but others will sicken and lie forever in English soil, with not a bullet fired.*

*Men everywhere sail across the Channel to fight. Ships hurl cannon balls into each other and men fall from them into the fathomless deep.*

The timber stores of Lynn are empty. Wood dark with age, as well as newer stock, has been sold, gone to Peterborough with a small army of carpenters to build the prisoner of war depot at Norman Cross.

There is little sympathy for the first prisoners even though they had been held on transport ships for four years. They are the French crew of the Réunion of Cherbourg which had been strafing British merchant shipping in the English Channel. Prisoners come walking across country too, from ships docking at Great Yarmouth. At first they are guarded by militia corps between camps in Norwich, East Dereham and Swaffham. They rarely try to flee. Escaping prisoners of war are always shot dead if they are caught.

In Raynham, Lord Townshend revels in his second military wind. He has long advocated a larger militia made up of volunteers to supplement a slimmer professional army. Now the country is nervous of war, the call for both is louder. Belatedly, the King sanctions the raising of foot and cavalry militia led by each county's Lord Lieutenant. This finds Lord Townshend in Norfolk and Philip Yorke, Earl of Hardwicke in Cambridgeshire calling on the superior men of each county to choose officers from their own circles and work down to all ranks.

Government funds provide equipment and uniforms, although some companies take pride in paying for their own.

Men who volunteer are paid a regulation sum according to rank for weekly training, and fined if they are absent for no good reason. Subscriptions to local funds sometimes offer bonus payments to volunteers as encouragement or to soften the financial burden of lack of wages on training days.

The great bonus of volunteering is that men are exempt from the local lotteries which raise a proportion of men at random for service if regular troops are scarce. Initially, companies serve for local defence, but soon they are commanded to march across Norfolk and beyond, serving for weeks or months to gain experience or fill weaknesses in other areas. Many are used to relieve regular forces stationed to maintain community order or to escort prisoners of war. As time progresses, even these volunteers are conscripted into regular forces.

Men with seagoing experience are a particular prize for the press gangs. Soon, the crews of merchant ships are rationed and inspected, to prevent extra men passing themselves off as essential crew, and regulations are passed that no British merchant ship can employ foreign nationals.

In May 1798, King's Lynn Corporation receive a command from the Admiralty to the effect that they must consent to a Rendezvous, or local gathering point, for pressing local men into the navy. Failure to consent makes Corporation members personally liable for sanction. The Rendezvous is established in a pub near St. Nicholas Church in the heart of the fishing and marine community. To avoid the probability that men will be rescued from detention by their friends and families, a ship is anchored out in the estuary to hold them until it is ready to sail to an appropriate station, prior to direct transfer to a naval vessel and service for an undetermined length of time.

**London**
**April 1801**

The King appoints the Earl of Hardwicke as his Lord Lieutenant of Ireland from April 1801 until November 1805. Hardwicke will be mostly in Dublin although he will return to Cambridgeshire periodically, but his attention will be on Irish matters. His responsibilities in Cambridgeshire are taken up by his Deputy Lord Lieutenants, including Richard Greaves Townley of Outwell.

Sir Thomas Hyde Page is sent to advise on repairs to harbours in Dublin and Wicklow, and to consult on building the Royal Canal between Dublin and the Shannon, and the Newry Canal.

## King's Lynn
## September 1801

> *I see the honeyed days of autumn bring Mylne and his son to Lynn. They command servants to carry their baggage but they mind their precious instruments themselves. Each day at sunrise they ride along my banks to South Lynn with Golborne. Then they strike out on narrow footpaths around fields towards Wiggenhall St. Germans. Men trudge after them, with carts full of wooden staves which they drive into the ground precisely where Mylne instructs, until the line of posts stretches all the way from South Lynn to Eau Brink.*

Robert Mylne invites Thomas Hyde Page to view the line on the ground before they go further. Hyde Page is working in Dublin so suggests that to save time, Golborne should trace the dimensions of the workings onto a large map which had been drawn to display the dimensions agreed in the Act of Parliament.

Later, back in London, Hyde Page receives several puzzling letters from Mylne. He examines his own copy of the same large map.

'It has all the measurements on it. We don't need anything else now but to compare it to the large map and make sure it's the same,' he tells Thomas Cubit, now his assistant.

Mylne writes that he wants to see Hyde Page's copy to compare it with the original large map which the Commissioners kept safe until passed to Mylne as a model of the work to be done. Hyde Page sends Cubit with his map to Mylne's office at New River Head, Clerkenwell, London, their headquarters of the New River Company.

'There's no need for me to see Page's map,' Mylne tells Cubit, having changed his mind. 'Here, compare it to the large map yourself, if you want to.'

When Mylne meets Hyde Page, he suggests dimensions at the Lynn end of the Cut which are different from those shown on the large map. His plan reduces the agreed width of waterway at the harbour end of the Cut by around a quarter from 480 feet to 364 feet.

'We cannot change these dimensions,' Hyde Page tells him. 'The change would be contrary to the Act of Parliament. In fact, the dimensions you suggest are, in my opinion, likely to be highly damaging to the harbour and dangerous to navigation.'

'The Act gives us discretionary powers, as the Engineers in charge, to make changes if we see fit,' Mylne argues.

'I agreed the dimensions in the Act. I see no need to change them, and I have no intention of doing so,' Hyde Page declares.

Afterwards, he writes to Mylne. 'I confirm that I wish to continue exactly as the Act lays down. I will come to New River Head to see the large map. I am convinced that the alterations you suggest will materially injure the navigation and harbour. I cannot consent to using the discretionary power referenced in the Act, because it requires changes to be made only in the presence of both of us. I will meet you in Lynn at your earliest convenience, and I will bring Mr. Cubit with me so that any changes we do agree can be noted on the spot.'

A week later, Hyde Page writes again. He is frustrated that having returned from defence work in Ireland a month early especially to settle the line at Lynn, no progress has been made.

'I must emphasise my opposition to the proposed changes which will narrow the channel more than it ought to be, according to my judgement. While you are free to make your own case to the Commissioners, I will not change my own opinion. We may have to ask the advice of the Commissioners at their next meeting to resolve this disagreeable indecision.'

After Christmas, Hyde Page is working in London with Cubit when a large package arrives from Mylne.

'The man has lost his senses! Listen to this. Mylne says he despairs of changing my opinion and he's sent his reasonings to justify his ideas. He says the efficient width of the Thames, with all its traffic, is about 750 feet while Lynn harbour is over 830 feet. He asks why should Lynn's river be wider than the Thames? And he's written out all the widths of the Thames from All Hallows to St. Catherine's Stairs.

Cubit smiles. 'After all the arguments surely nobody would want to meddle with what's been agreed. Anyway, has he compared the distances to their estuaries? The Thames and the Great Ouse are quite different.'

'Well of course they are. Then he debates the meaning of the word 'model' as if it is just a starting point, not the final decision. And this!' Hyde Page waves a sheet of verse at Cubit.

'He quotes from Shakespeare's Bardolph. "When we mean to build we first survey the plot, then draw the model..."'

'He means to persuade you, then!' Cubit laughed.

'It's no laughing matter,' Hyde Page says, aggrieved.

'And this! He's sent a copy of a minute from a Bedford Level meeting addressed to the Committee promoting the Eau Brink Bill. They say they are unanimously resolved that while they think every reasonable precaution should be taken to preserve Lynn harbour, they are seriously apprehensive that if the Cut is too wide, it will not clear the sands as expected.'

'Wasn't that before the Act was agreed, when everybody was putting forward different points of view?'

'Yes. Damn the man. This is a complete waste of time when I have more pressing matters to deal with. The Ordnance wants me back in Dublin, but I won't put up with this nonsense. If Mylne wants dimensions, I'll give him dimensions. Give me that copy of the Act of Parliament. He'll get quotations too,' Hyde Page fumed. 'The Commissioners should know about this and direct proceedings from now on.'


## Downham Market
## January 1802

Mr. Lemmon receives a letter from Robert Mylne to pass onto the Commissioners. It is a detailed account of the benefits of his plan compared to Hyde Page's unfortunate refusal to accept changes.

'Lynn harbour is too wide,' he claims. 'Jetties will be needed to direct water into a narrower stream to create a deep channel. Hence it is useless to make the trench of the Cut a width to suit a harbour which is intended to be narrowed.

'My plan can be executed within the funds available because less needs to be excavated by workmen and the remainder can be removed by dredger. I estimate just under £40,000, compared to the original Golborne and Watté estimate of over £52,000.

'The wording of the Act uses the phrase 'not less than' fifty or one hundred feet for the banks and forelands. Therefore, they may be 'more than' fifty or one hundred feet. I recommend the banks should be increased to give a narrower course within the same overall distance between the banks. Sir Thomas Hyde Page will not give this his consideration. He insists the only acceptable dimensions are what the map specifies.

'If the banks are set out at the agreed distance, it would be easy to widen the Cut hereafter, but if found too wide, it would be impossible to contract it, and there is no doubt that it would be found too wide if made as Sir Thomas insists.

'I leave it to the Commissioners to consider and I will readily attend any meeting to afford assistance to their determinations,' he offers.

Mr. Lemmon finds himself batting letters between the engineers and the Commissioners.

Mylne tries to visit both Hyde Page and Sir Martin Browne Folkes in London, but neither is at home. Then he finds Browne Folkes at the Houses of Parliament and has a long discussion with him there, generously granting time away from other important work, he says, because the Commissioners are demanding the issue is progressed.

In the middle of March, Hyde Page reports to the Eau Brink Commissioners. He confirms his agreement to the wording of the Act and points out that Mylne also agreed as late as 26th November 1801, but had changed his mind by January 1802. He adds,

'Mylne's suggestion that the width of the Thames is a suitable comparison for the Great Ouse is misleading. The materially different distances between the widths measured and the mouths of the rivers, respectively thirty miles for the Thames and only three miles from Lynn harbour to the Deeps, creates differences in the strength of the tides at the point where the widths are measured.

'Most critically, if the width of 364 feet by Mylne's plan suddenly expands into the harbour of over 800 feet, it doesn't take an engineer to perceive that the incoming tide would be suddenly checked as it enters the Cut, causing increasing shoals. It would create a torrent through the narrow Cut that is too great for the navigation upon it. The country should pause a little before such serious consequences are risked.

'Regarding estimates, none are proper if they are made to suit an inadequate fund. Mylne has left a third of the work with the idea it can be performed by a machine. This would soon fail to operate at all in the Cut much less remove the bar of the river's natural bottom for three miles.'

Hyde Page is working on strengthening Dublin harbour, which prevents him attending the next Commissioners meeting at the end of March. In a letter to Mr. Lemmon, he confirms that he means to discharge the trust put on him by the Act of Parliament in the most conscientious way. He has no other motive than the benefit of the country, as he has no intention to accept any salary or reward beyond expenses. He has no doubt that the Ordnance will give permission for him to see the Cut set out on the ground with Mr. Mylne, provided he observes the dimensions printed in the Act.

Hyde Page's position as a military engineer, loaned from the Ordnance to the Eau Brink project by the Act is proving to be a problem. He is paid a salary as a Royal Engineer and does not accept other paid work unless he asks permission of the King or Master of the Ordnance. This drawn-out discussion with Mylne brings into question whether his time here is an unnecessary diversion of scarce resources in wartime.

The Eau Brink Commissioners meeting in April 1802 resolves to ask the two engineers to nominate a third person to settle the difference between them. Hyde Page questions if this is permitted by the Act, and provided that can be confirmed by a legal authority, he offers the names of three military engineers.

Meanwhile, Mylne complains to Mr. Lemmon that at the rate and manner of sending letters between them, he fears there will be more difficulty in settling an umpire than leading off the flood and drainage waters of the Ouse through Lynn to the sea. Sarcasm satisfied, he replies that he can't agree to any of Hyde Page's three nominations. Two of them are known to him as previously having been acquainted with Eau Brink business, and he doesn't know the third. He does know of a civil engineer who would be equal to the task but doesn't name him, and suggests if he doesn't suit, then he will give up all hope of any other who would be found to fit.

The next meeting of the Eau Brink Commissioners hears the legal opinion of George Wilson of Lincoln's Inn, who determines that the Act is clear and precise as to the dimensions, and the engineers are bound to follow what it says. Wilson judges they have no power to call in a third party to put a different construction on the dimensions stated in the Act. He advises that if the two engineers continue to differ, having been required to proceed with the Cut by the Commissioners, a writ can be granted to compel them to do so. Ultimately, if they still refuse, both might be fined. Wilson thinks it most likely though, that a court will offer some form of mediation. By 26th August 1802, both Hyde Page and Mylne have been served with the formal requirement to proceed.

**Downham Market**
**September 1802**

Hyde Page sets out for Downham Market but by 8th September, nothing has been heard from Mylne. Hyde Page decides to set out the line without him and asks Mr. Golborne to join him there. On the same day, Mylne writes from his home in Amwell, Hertfordshire, saying that letters have crossed and not enough time has been allowed for him to get to Lynn, to action what is not agreed. This is not his way of doing business, he states.

Mylne directs Mr Golborne to set out the middle line as he himself can't leave London due to pressure of work that must be completed before the rains set in. He doesn't think workers will be found anyway, as the harvest is in progress. On 12th September, Mylne tells Mr. Lemmon that he plans to come soon, to set out the dimensions as he himself sees fit, so that Commissioners may inspect the differences and decide the way forward.

Hyde Page is staying at Hillington Hall, Lynn, the home of Sir Martin Browne Folkes. By 20th September, Golborne has sufficient labourers and starts the work which takes several days.

Mr. Lemmon reports progress to Mylne and tells him the Commissioners will meet again on 14th October. He expects Hyde Page will stay until then, and invites Mylne to join them. Meanwhile, could he examine the line of the Cut and say if it meets his approval.

Hyde Page attends the October meeting with Thomas Cubit as his assistant. He says if Mr. Mylne perseveres in his endeavours to introduce a new plan, it is for the Commissioners to determine what further steps should be taken. If this is the case, he feels it is impossible to proceed further, short of an alteration in the Act of Parliament.

The Commissioners formally approve the plan as set out in the Act, and ask Mr. Golborne to attend on 15th November 1802 to report on Mylne's inspection of the line. By January 1803, Mylne still refuses to agree with the line set out by Hyde Page. He nominates Captain Joseph Huddart as his preferred umpire.

**The Lamb Inn, Ely.**
**April 1803**

In April, Commissioners chaired by Lionel Self, then Mayor of Lynn, with Sir Martin Browne Folkes and several Lynn Aldermen, receive a letter from Hyde Page explaining that he cannot agree to Huddart as he is a close associate of Mylne's, they being frequent collaborators on engineering projects and both Brothers of Trinity House, known to them all as the foremost authority on lighthouse and marine safety.

The Commissioners are forced to make an application to the King's Bench in May 1804. Extended discussions take place between Mylne and Hyde Page and Huddart is eventually appointed as umpire.

Huddart surveys in the summer but he chooses neither plan. He recommends extending the Cut further at both ends, bringing it closer to the harbour. The width of 484 feet specified in the Act, reduced to 364 feet by Mylne, shrinks under Huddart to 296 feet at the lower junction of the Cut with the River Great Ouse. In addition, he recommends the trench be changed from a straight sided to a concave profile. The Commissioners, now tied by the preceding arguments and desperate to break the stalemate between the two engineers, accept Huddart's plan.

*The old man and the soldier used to share their ideas with other engineers but now, they have nothing to say to each other. The soldier is called abroad to defend the country against a new threat of invasion. The old man is vindictive. He calls the soldier incompetent behind his back. They fight with fierce words in the High Court and each claims they have saved their reputations. I wait. I watch. Nothing changes for me.*

## King's Lynn
## Spring 1803

Mayor Lionel Self is grim as he formally announces from the steps of Trinity Guildhall that Britain is now officially at war with France. All coastal towns will have to prepare. There's an embargo on French and Dutch ships here, and the ports of Belgium and Holland as well as France are closed to us, even for supplies.

'Will there be new recruiting for the army?' men shout from the crowd gathered to hear him.

'There's rumours of a county registration so there could be a ballot if invasion becomes a real threat. It'll be volunteers for a while. We'll have to wait and see.'

Travellers from Holland describe Napoleon's massive invasion preparations being made across the channel. In every shipyard, vessels are being built to carry forces across the sea, and they are queuing in river mouths, armed and ready. French men are flocking to join the fight. Fields are turned into tent cities with thousands of them under training.

There is no attempt to hide their plans. Napoleon intends to invade Britain, and he's positioned his army at Boulogne in plain view of English telescopes to put the fear of God into the British.

In July, a Military Service Bill calls for the County Lieutenants to compile registers of men in their counties to be trained, armed and ready for service anywhere in Great Britain. Merchant shipping and barge crews can get exemption from service but the numbers permitted on each vessel are sparse and have to be made up of old men and youths who are not eligible for service because of their age. Almost all the merchants, colliers and fishing fleet ships are armed with guns. Most are old war relics, but they'd put a hole in a Frenchman if needs be.

Coastal towns draw together lists of volunteers for a corps of Sea Fencibles to patrol the coast and raise an early alarm if the enemy is sighted. They must harass and delay them for as long as possible. Sea Fencibles will be close to home, but they'll be sitting ducks for a well-trained force with superior arms, which the French certainly are.

Flagpoles are raised at key points, including Raynham, Holkham and Houghton Halls, on which red flags will be hoisted if the enemy is seen off the coast or actually makes a landing.

Barge owners are asked to be ready to evacuate local civilians away from the coast, and transport troops if necessary. Nobility, yeomen and gentry who own horses, carts and waggons are asked to make them available with their drivers, and anyone with horse fodder is asked to donate it. Millers and bakers are asked to ensure a regular supply of flour and bread. If an invasion occurs, those with property are instructed to destroy it rather than leave it for the enemy to use.

## King's Lynn
## July 1803

The assembled Corporation of King's Lynn listen to a letter from Lord Townshend read by Edmund Rolfe Elsden. On an order from the Secretary of State for War, the Admiralty instructs authorities of all maritime counties to co-operate in providing for the defence of the country.

'It can only mean they judge an invasion is close,' Rolfe Elsden concludes.

'I don't envy your year, Elsden, it may be a bumpy ride,' Lionel Self commiserates, relieved that he has completed his year as Mayor in favour of Rolfe Elsden's second term. 'What are they asking for?'

'They want us to provide armed vessels for hire to the Admiralty. They're to be manned and commanded by the Sea Fencibles, who must be trained in the use of the guns.'

'How many do they want? We can't afford to have good ships standing idle when they should be on voyages.'

'Enough for all enrolled Fencibles to be occupied. If more men are enrolled than we have vessels for, the Government say they will supply more vessels. As well as that, they're asking for merchant and collier vessels of around 150 tons to be equipped with four guns, two fore and two aft, and they'll provide the ammunition.'

Vice Admiral William Bentinck of Terrington St. Clement is in command of the Lynn Sea Fencibles, whose area covers from Fosdyke to Cromer.

'Vice Admiral Bentinck told me yesterday that enrolment for the Sea Fencibles will start here next week and elsewhere as soon as he's seen the various Mayors in his area. Once the men are enrolled, his first order is to assess the coast for likely landing places.'

'We should put out the word immediately. Men will have to prepare to sign up.'

'The press gangs are very active around the Rendezvous by St. Nicholas Church,' Lionel Self tells the gathering. 'Men will be reluctant to come into town, even if they're supposed to be protected.'

'The Corporation should have a small committee to liaise with the Fencible commanders,' Councillor Taylor suggests, 'made up of those not already occupied with the territorial volunteers. Alderman Everard and I are frequently away on Volunteer Infantry exercises.'

'Agreed. Offers please, gentlemen?'

Rolfe Elsden selects all who raise their hands. It could be a long and testing assignment.

Napoleon Bonaparte's invasion plans have materialised into thousands of small watercraft at his disposal in the ports and rivers of France, Belgium and Holland. His army are well drilled and disciplined as a result of weeks of waiting for the command to proceed. His plentiful stores of ammunition and food are assembled. His herds of horses are stabled nearby and his cannon all but primed. He is coming.

The traders are practical men. Speed was never more important. If a crossing is successful on the south coast, the French could get to Lynn within a day or so by sea, always assuming they don't come across the North Sea to start with, and they would benefit from a ready-made distribution network to the major eastern towns.

'How many ships are already armed?'

'How many wagons do we have to evacuate civilians and for troop transport?'

'What stocks of flour do we hold?'

Every question spawns a score more.

'Are they armed to the Admiralty's requirements?'

'Where is a safe place to evacuate women and children to?'

As time passes, the most insistent question becomes 'What must we destroy to prevent it falling into enemy hands? Food stocks? Carriages? Farm animals? Jetties and landings?'

For some, these extreme directions amount to community destruction, and no panic generating edict from Government would persuade them that these so called temporary hardships would lead to long lasting wellbeing as free citizens.

*I sense their jitters. They're told a vicious, hungry army is coming. Those that can take off for Marshland, convinced no soldier would bother going there, on the road to an impenetrable shore. Some rush to Ely with a long buried remembrance of old warriors holding out against foreign invaders. A few go far north to the old wall and its rugged Celtic defenders who clung to their ground till death itself robbed them.*

*Most look at their leaking hovels, their damp earthen floors and mildewed truckles, but they see a safe resting place, a glimpse of a cheery fire grate, a stew-pot hung there bubbling with scraggy vegetables that they've grown in their own square yard of mud, and they draw their children round. They tell them to stay close, but to scarper like rats if they see a blue uniform. Go hide by the river, they tell their daughters, hide under its water with a hollow reed to breathe through if need be. The river will save you.*

*Men and their wives look at each other with long glances and distant memories of their fresh youth. They share unspoken promises to defend as long as they can, as long as they live.*

*Women arm themselves. Some with knives hidden in their skirts, some with brandy and rouge, but most with denial, a side-step of consciousness, a straw against reality. For if they survive there may soon be babies needing to be fed. The bastards of hostiles, off-spring with little fondness to nurture them, protected only by their innocence.*

Ladies instruct servants to clear cellars, lay up candles, food and ships biscuits, bandages and laudanum, fit for a siege. If the worst comes they'll hide there. If necessary they'll escape through dark passages to the riverside and row with muffled oars till they are beyond the enemy camp fires, each to their family's church and supposed security of their forebears.

'We are rather lacking in useful things to do in this effort,' Mrs. Everard remarks to the Ladies Committee.

They open a fund for warm clothing. Sufficient is donated for more than 800 vests. Lynn's High Street tailors sell ready-cut flannel vest pieces in various sizes for society ladies to complete in sewing afternoons, which are immediately distributed to the Lynn Loyal Volunteers to protect them from the winter winds.

## King's Lynn
## September 1804

Vice Admiral William Bentinck's Sea Fencible Captain is Joseph Bullen, a Navy veteran of the American War of Independence and numerous other campaigns. Captain Bullen is a formidably lucky man. He and Horatio Nelson were two of only twenty seven men left alive out of a force of over 200 who survived tropical fevers in an expedition to create a naval base at San Juan, in present day Nicaragua. Since then, multiple severe injuries have prevented his active service, but he feels restored when at sea and when he can't get a ship, he volunteers.

'Have the men been trained in manoeuvres?' Bentinck asks him.

'I would say not. They're skilled at working their own vessels, of course, but not together as a force, except by familiarity with each other. Nelson told me he thinks they could be made indispensable. He thinks there should be two lines along the coast. Royal Navy vessels should be close by the French, while the Fencibles should stay close to the landing areas here. If the men are trained to work as one, we will be invincible,' Bullen asserts.

'We should have smaller groups, each led by a petty officer, and those officers will give the orders, instead of waiting for a single man's command to filter down the ranks and across the distances. It means the group will react more quickly, and that could be crucial,' Bentinck orders.

'The crews will see logic in that. We'll be ready when they come,' Bullen assures him.

## Marshland
## 1805

The activities of the Eau Brink Commission continue to suffer from the higher priorities of national defence against Napoleon Bonaparte. Meetings are frequently inquorate, and dominated by the failure to collect taxes. Even John Watté has to resort to threatening court action if his invoice is not paid, but the floods this year are so extensive that the Commissioners are forced into action. They renew the 1795 Act in August and appoint John Rennie to report on the state of drainage in the South and Middle Levels. He works with James Golborne and presents his report the next August.

Negotiations start on purchasing land required for the Cut. Few owners accept the first offer made by the Eau Brink Commissioners, including John Cary who refuses £657. Reverend R. Hankinson, Vicar of Walpole St. Andrew refuses £329 for himself and on behalf of the parish patron, Thomas Hankinson Esq., he refuses £898.

Sea Fencibles are training all around the coast. Navy vessels patrol the channel day and night. The British people are resolved, and Napoleon, now Emperor of France, knows it.

He tries but fails to divert the British Navy elsewhere and his generals report that troops will soon run short of supplies. Weather in the Channel will deteriorate as autumn approaches. Both could endanger his planned invasion.

He decides to inspect his flotilla of small boats and rafts in the open sea, against the advice of his naval commanders. The waters are rough and a storm threatens. Thirty barges succumb to the waves and scores of troops perish.

Napoleon hesitates. To his rear, the British allies are co-ordinating their efforts to expel the French from lands they recently gained in Europe. Austria, his supposed ally, has joined them. He has to choose. Take Britain or keep Europe?

He orders his hundreds of thousands of troops at Boulogne to strike camp and head to Austria, which surrenders to him on 19th October 1805. Two days later, the British Navy, led by Admiral Nelson, destroys the Franco-Spanish fleet in the Cape of Trafalgar. Without them Napoleon's forces can no longer threaten British shores.

Bullen, tight lipped and ashen, joins his Sea Fencible men back in Lynn. Deliverance from the French exhilarates them, but seamen everywhere reflect that success was achieved by the sacrifice of an irreplaceable leader. Many local mariners had served with Nelson, or heard of his manner from others. They tell of how he inspired devotion to duty by unconventional means, his skilful seamanship and his respectful manner towards ordinary seamen. He was a Norfolk boy too, born at Burnham Thorpe not far from Lynn, so even those who didn't know him identified with him and felt his character rubbed off on them. He was the best of the best.

'I'm leaving for London,' Bullen tells them. You'll be all right while I'm gone.'

'Are you going to the funeral?' they ask.

'I'll be wherever I can serve but I hope to be at St. Paul's.'

Bullen's voice cracks. He is among scores of hardened men who wipe cuffs past their faces in the streets that day. He and

Nelson had survived so much together, knew how the other thought and were strong with the other nearby. But bereft as he feels, Bullen is still a leader, and will lead as Nelson led. He tightens his jaw. 'I'll be back soon.'

Within a year, Napoleon takes Vienna, disrupts the coalition forces of Prussia and Russia at Austerlitz and brings Prussia under French dominance at the Battles of Jena and Auerstedt. The French army marches into Berlin on 27th October 1806.

## London
## 1807

The London salons buzz with new voices. They tell of harrowing flights from Berlin and wider afield in Europe before the onslaught of Napoleon's troops, certain imprisonment or worse. One of these is Dr. Charles Brown, past physician in London and Carmarthen, then via Russia to physician at the court of King Frederick William III of Prussia, trusted to ensure the safe escape of King Frederick William's Queen Louise. He had joined the King at the battle at Jena as his Prussian Generals reported their losses and it became clear that Prussia had fallen into Napoleon Bonaparte's grip. Dr. Brown was sent back to England with letters addressed to King George III and Queen Charlotte, with news of the military reversals for the allied forces, and King Frederick William's personal assurance to Queen Charlotte that her niece, his own Queen Louise, had reached safety.

They are joined in London society by men leaving the service of the Honourable East India Company, whose contracts had been changed by Government direction in a bid to prevent corruption. In future they were to be paid a fixed salary, rather than making their livings by commission on the goods they handled, which promised much slimmer returns.

Among them is Thomas Hoseason, an ex-Navy Purser originally from the Shetland Islands, who had been responsible for supplying ship provisions in the East Indies Squadron. He negotiated contracts for rum and wine along with Basil Cochrane, a senior Honourable East India Company merchant in Madras, and married Cochrane's orphaned niece Angelica. He became acquainted with Lord William Bentinck, then Governor of Madras, who was a cousin of Vice Admiral Bentinck of Terrington St. Clement. Thomas is almost certain to know Sir Andrew Snape Hamond, naval veteran of the American War of Independence and now Comptroller for the British Navy at Somerset House, soon to retire. Thomas and Angelica are now living at her late father's house in Harley Street, London, where Thomas becomes a financial factotum for the wealthy. His attention is drawn to the low price of land, and the possibility that it could increase very soon.

## The River Great Ouse
## Summer 1808

*I am bewildered by the new men who come from far-away lands to look at me. They speak of frozen Russian plains and magnificent courts in Europe, of hot lands dripping in jewels and long voyages to rebellious dominions with vast forests.*

*Three of them paid fortunes for fields here. None are farmers, river men or merchants. These men are far from the bloom of life, and have grown used to fine living. They do not know me and they will struggle to learn my ways.*

*Two build mansions that dwarf the sturdy houses around them. The one whose house is within my winter's grasp sends for trees that won't thrive in my land. Another builds a jetty in my path across from the town. These men do not see horizons that limit them, but mere hindrances to be pushed aside. They speak of crop values and drainage, of improvements and new roads. They worry me.*

Mr. Thomas Hoseason and Sir Andrew Snape Hamond trot their horses along the bank of the river at the boundary of Dr. Charles Brown's newly acquired estate in Clenchwarton, a little inland of West Lynn. Several small rowing boats make way for a barge with a gang of five heading for Downham Market. They won't reach Wiggenhall before the tide starts to fall, so they're unlikely to go much further upriver today.

'It's a well throated river, right enough, and busy, but it doesn't seem anything like the destructive force Vice Admiral Bentinck claims it to be,' Charles Brown observes.

'Don't be deceived,' Snape Hamond cautions. A few weeks of rain and a north wind is all it takes for these waters to destroy anything you might hope for. My estate in Terrington should be safe, but Bentinck warns we must maintain the drains and river banks if we are to prosper.'

'But imagine,' Thomas enthuses. 'If these fields can be free of flood and all this foreshore put to crops, imagine how productive they will be. Once the river's cut off and drained, the land will soon restore and be safe evermore. We'll need to push the locals to press for the Cut and it'll take a year or two, but we'll soon see returns on our investments.'

'My farm manager doesn't reckon the Cut will ever be built. He says there's too much opposition.'

'The Commissioners already have sufficient authority. They could set it in train tomorrow,' Snape Hamond reminds Dr. Brown.

'But if they don't have the funds, and use all their receipts just to keep up the banks? It's a vicious circle.'

'They need expert financial advice,' Hoseason declares. If they wait till they have money in hand then no, it won't ever get built. I went to a Commissioner's meeting last year to judge the potential for improvement, before I purchased Shetland Farm. Now I own estate here, I can be a Commissioner myself and begin to steer events. You could both join me. Then we'll know how to manage our own funds for the highest return.'

**Clenchwarton**
**January 1809**

Dr. Charles and Mary Brown are assembling their home with new furniture from London, but their drawing room is already comfortable with a substantial fire in the hearth. Along with many others, their treasures were left behind as they fled before Napoleon Bonaparte's rapidly advancing forces. Within hours of arrival, the Grande Armée had ransacked every mansion and house in Berlin, taking anything of value. King Frederick William's palace at Charlottenburg was ruined. It would be a sad place to return to now, but Charles would go in a flash, if there was peace.

He shivers despite his bedroom being the warmest the house has to offer. The weather has turned freezing cold, worsened by frequent torrential rain. He calls for more fuel to stoke the fire. His wife Mary returns to bed at noon.

'It's the only place I feel warm. I only hope that wretch Napoleon is freezing too,' she says with uncharacteristic venom. 'The scandal of it, putting the likes of us and thousands of others out of their cosy homes.'

Charles agrees. Life has become inconvenient since they left Berlin. He knows Mary is trying hard to become accustomed to village life, but it is far from what they'd grown used to. She furnished their house in Berlin with the most tasteful decor, and she loved providing the homely hospitality which made the 'English Doctor's house' the place to be. They offered a welcome open door to anyone in Berlin to visit the King and his ministers. Supper and a turn of cards or sightseeing trips in the countryside introduced all manner of interesting people who knew the latest news, fashions and novels. Now, there are fewer guests with less time to spare, and their local friends were always flitting down to London to renew their social activities.

This cold has hung on for weeks. Last week there was a heavy snowfall, and just as its thaw waters began to seep through to the river, there was a tremendous storm. The river is swollen and tears at the banks, rendering long stretches useless at containing water which backs up through the entire area, flooding hundreds of acres. Cattle are lost and houses undermined. It is a sodden, miserable place. Mary would much rather be in Carmarthen with her old friends or with their daughters in London. For Charles's sake though, she keeps quiet. She suspects the change is a challenge for him too.

Charles rises quietly so as not to wake Mary. It is early, but he is weary from a fretful night. His brain has sprinted from woe to woe. His ambitions as a country squire are dissolving in a mess of reality. Yesterday, his estate manager warned him the river banks were frozen solid and fractured. It's only the ice in them that's preventing them breaking down. When the thaw comes they'll reveal their weakness, and he needs to employ a gang of men to repair them.

This winter seems never ending. It had been colder in Krichev when he was there as medical director of the Russian Army, but somehow it had not seemed as dispiriting as these past weeks. Was it the busyness of his work there that kept him distracted, or the camaraderie he wonders. Perhaps it is the damp mists here that chill every sinew of his body and mind. His estate workers just shrug off the icy fields and having to lug extra feed for the horses. Their house maid seems almost pleased to have extra fires to tend.

'Keep it cheery,' she urges, giving him a bright smile, but Brown's accounts tell a different story, of greater spend, falling income and diminishing reserves.

Brown sighs. For the hundredth time he asks himself how he had misjudged this place so critically that he had been persuaded to come here at all, let alone to purchase extra strips of riverside from his neighbours with the additional maintenance costs.

Yes, it is true that when the river is diverted and its old bed sold as productive land, he will see his fortunes improve, but that won't happen until all the current military adventures are concluded, if they ever are.

He cracks open the heavy curtains. Dawn is breaking. Above, the sky is lightening to purple. Towards Lynn, against a brighter horizon, the clouds are a luminous coral and for a moment he is astonished by their beauty. They are ablaze behind a silhouette of black laced trees. Gulls are cavorting in groups as they fly inland from their marshy roosts, and for a moment he is back in Berlin at a Palace Ball where he remembers Queen Louise wore a satin dress that exact shade of pink. There was conversation, fine wine and delicacies served on silver platters, music and dancing, and Mary's mischievous laughter.

Within minutes the brilliant vista fades to a dove grey against a gentle blue infinity, but he is gladdened and it gives him resolve.

He determines to sell his considerable library which still rests in his old Carmarthen house. He'll sort out his favourites to bring here to read, so he can disguise his pressing financial motive and he thinks this will prevent Mary having any cause to worry.

**King's Lynn**
**5th October 1810**

> *I am dizzy with vessels flitting across me. No more the neat ships that dock tidily along my wharf side. Now a seething jostle, each hindering others, an ill disciplined scramble to unload their cargoes.*
>
> *Ferries ply across me. I lap at their overburdened decks, wetting the shoes of workers returning from Marshland's autumn harvest fields as they ready to jump back onto land. Now a ship's mooring ropes obstruct the ferry landing and the raft snags on a tangle of hemp and chain, violently tipping its passengers into my waters.*
>
> *I sweep along, grabbing some in my arms. They flail and kick to reach the shore. My undercurrent holds to those who scream and cough in panic, and those*

*with life blood pouring from their heads. Some are pulled from me, but the rest, the chosen ten, I carry swiftly a full league to my estuary.*

*They wail after their children, after their lovers. I am unconcerned, for they are mere specks that my creatures will feed on. It is my nature.*

*Men design to harm. They send armies to hunt each other. Still, their eyes are turned away from me.*

Charles Brown's new residence has announced its own hazards. It was a mercy that none of the Marshland families had been caught on the ferry but as it was the only route into Lynn that avoided the long detour to Wiggenhall St. Germans bridge, there was a real risk of another incident in which they might not be so fortunate. Mary Brown resolves she will never use the ferry again.

Brown and Hoseason meet with Vice Admiral Bentinck and urge him to call a meeting at the Ferry House, West Lynn, to devise some sort of plan.

'It's safe enough, if the boatmen take good care,' Bentinck says, 'but it's often overloaded. King's Lynn Corporation give licences to the ferry men, and insist on improvements each time there's a problem, but they're soon forgotten. We need a way to hold the ferry man and other parties to their word. Otherwise, no matter what effort is put in, its effects will be short lived.'

Word spreads rapidly. During an impromptu meeting at The Ferry House, worried Marshlanders demand safer operations. Bentinck, Snape Hamond and Hoseason find themselves volunteering to draw up draft revised regulations, with Brown acting as treasurer.

A formal Ferry Boat Committee chaired by Joseph Taylor, Mayor of Lynn, in February 1812 resolves there should be two passenger boats and one for horses in constant use, with a notice of the maximum number of people or horses to be carried and a visible line to show the maximum depth to which it ought to float. Fares are doubled to one penny per person and four pennies for a horse plus rider. A committee of seven is formed comprised of two persons nominated by the Mayor, two nominated by the lessee of the ferry boat and three from the public, to hear complaints and take steps to remedy abuses.

By early summer, Vice Admiral William Bentinck is with the Baltic fleet during efforts to create an alliance of forces against France. He has distant family relations in the Russian court, and is acquainted with Crown Prince Bernadotte of Sweden. He makes several secret journeys between Stockholm and St. Petersburg and in August, a treaty is signed by which Sweden joins the British-Russian alliance. It is not known by whose authority he brought the parties together or if it was on his own initiative. He overwinters at St. Petersburg where he succumbs to typhus and dies in February 1813.


**King's Lynn**
**22nd July 1814**

> *I echo to the peal of bells in towns and villages along my path. Their enemy is vanquished, exiled to an island in the Mediterranean Sea. Peace has come. People flock to their churches and sing in thanksgiving.*
>
> *At night torches are lit, lanterns and candles shine out from every window. Fireworks burst in showers of limelight. My waters flash in response, I am a river of diamonds, bright rubies and emeralds. I twinkle from bank to bank.*

The ladies of Lynn have been boiling hundreds of plum puddings for today's celebrations. Over 6,000 of the poorer folk of the area are to be served a meal of mutton, bread and plum pudding at tables in the Tuesday Market Place.

The timber merchants send teams with tables and benches. The bakers work through the night and a fruity aroma spreads over the town in a mouth-watering antidote to years of shortages. Scores of barrels of beer are rolled out from The Globe and the gentlemen of the town, led by Mayor Taylor are assembled. Today, the gentry serve the poor people. But the question of the moment is 'Will the peace last?'

## The River Great Ouse
## 1815

*I shudder, deep down beyond my bed. The ancient ground is changing, swirling, bubbling. A great power is massing. It seeks release like a throbbing boil. Birds take flight, wild animals scatter. The earth roars like a thousand cannon as rocks explode, shooting boiling gas high into the sky, as elemental as creation itself. A fountain of crimson fire spews molten rock onto men and beast. It is a chimney of hell.*

*Animals stampede with terror in their eyes. They fall, buried in thick ash. Men and women run with blood running from their ears, their heads and their bodies. They are disorientated by sound, and do not hear their own screams.*

*The air fills with choking black smoke. It reaches out to touch the sun and the earth turns midnight dark. The sun does not light the next day, nor the next week. The world grows cold. Heavy rain penetrates the fog. It poisons the ground with a lethal acid. Young grasses die. Blossom is heavy with grey ash, with few insects to pollinate it. Trees wither.*

*I tickle when flurries of snow settle on me, thrown from a coppered pewter sky. They lodge in the vegetation on the banks, spinning a fine lacy trim to my brown waters. It cloaks the ground, making it crisp and tidy. Soon bigger flakes prick icy sharp. I absorb their infinite patterns and become colder, till I grow plaques of ice that float and crash together.*

*Creatures become heavy, too cold to feel. Every step is a test of trust. Only an occasional plod of hooves and rattling bridle ventures into the muffling snow.*

*I am silent, discrete below the whiteout, a master, servile in the presence of a mightier power. Every living thing, every spirit, is hunkered down.*

*My waters become sharp. Frogspawn shrivels, insect larvae die in their eggs. Fish that should be hunting are suspended as if living dead. Young eels do not come. They are lost in the chaos of currents.*

*The sky presses down, a primordial bruise of mauve bucking clouds that turn at dusk into a ceiling of the damned: purple, blazing orange and blood red.*

Fenland farmers are stricken. The sky changes to a dirty yellow and crops are covered in grey dust. The older field workers sometimes struggle to breathe, it is so oppressive. It is too cold for corn to swell. The farmers swear they have never known such a poor harvest, the yield is disastrous. In late summer they hear reports that a huge volcanic explosion on the far side of the earth is responsible. It's said it is the largest eruption in human history and many thousands are dead on the Indonesian archipelago. Farmers have no precedent to help manage their land, except to hope the dust will blow away before long.

**Waterloo, Belgium**
**18th June 1815**

*I taste blood. The British allies form ranks against the French dictator, newly escaped from his island prison and supported by his old troopers. When they battle on the sodden fields of Belgium, the spirit of life drains from men and horses, thousands upon thousands of them, enough to tincture the streams of Europe and enrich the tides of the North Sea.*

*Some of the courageous return. They are quiet, with the trauma of what they've witnessed, for many left their comrades lying in foreign ground. They wonder at the thankful nation they saved from cruel domination, for now that the dictator is sent to the most distant rock on earth, troops have turned overnight from valuable assets to needy liabilities, from paid to pauper.*

### The Griffin Inn, March, Cambridgeshire
### August 1815

The Eau Brink Commissioners gather with renewed vigour. They now include Thomas Hoseason, along with Sir Andrew Snape Hamond, Charles Brown and Reverend Ambrose Goode, the recently appointed Vicar of Terrington St. Clement. Reverend Goode leads a prayer of thanks that the Battle of Waterloo has finally ended the war. Then Sir Andrew Snape Hamond takes up the previous meeting's discussions.

'The Cut is absolutely necessary but it cannot be executed without applying to Parliament for a longer period to collect taxes than is provided under the current Act. Now that life will return to normal, we should start to draw up an application for an extension in the next session.'

'We should issue notices to quit. Tenants will need time to arrange their business if we mean to give notice for next Lady Day in March,' Thomas Hoseason suggests.

Mr. Lemmon reminds the Commissioners that the Corporation of Lynn has failed to maintain banks along land that belongs to them and it is a severe burden on the Eau Brink accounts.

Sir Thomas Hare, whose farm income is badly reduced by river overflows around Stow, knew there had been an arrangement in place for the Corporation to contribute a proportion of the cost, but they haven't paid for years.

'We should not indebt our accounts to maintain the upkeep of these banks unless the proportions are fair,' Dr. Brown voices the verdict of them all and they set about recovering the dues.

By October, the financial news is less encouraging. Far from life returning to normal as they had expected, taxes are about to be raised to address the massive debt incurred by the war. Over 350,000 men are demobbed. Wages fall, it being easy to obtain labour at any low rate, but despite this, most returners cannot not find employment.


## Marshland
## 1816

In spring, the air is so cold that young lambs perish in great numbers. Germinating corn is frosted, staying short and thin. Vegetables are stunted, cattle are going hungry. Many complain about the taste of water and say it is making them sick. They wait for relief in the summer, but the skies look like steel. Warmth simply does not come

Food stocks are exhausted. Corn that fell in price at the end of the war is now so expensive that families are going hungry. Prices are kept high by a government tariff on imports to protect rich farmers. In London, there is fear that agitators will find willing audiences among the hungry, badly paid and resentful populace. Men appeal for cheaper flour and a return to the meagre pay they need to survive. News from the manufacturing towns is of disturbances and machine breaking in factories. Food riots are reported from Suffolk and Essex. When disturbances spread to Norwich, local Justices of the Peace and militia commanders prepare for commotions.

## Downham Market
## 1816

Sir Thomas Hare has charge of the Clackclose troop of the Norfolk Yeomanry in Downham Market and he reminds his men they may be called upon to quell civil unrest. In June, he and John Thurlow Dering of Crow Hall, Denver, come face to face with the anger of the crowd in one of the worst protest incidents to take place in Norfolk.

Thomas Hoseason is a now a Justice of the Peace for Marshland. He is keen to know what occurred because he fears he might have to manage the same type of incident. When the Justices meet, Dering is clearly still shaken and holds back from talking about it, but Hoseason persuades him to tell him more.

'It had been quite straightforward to start with,' Dering says. 'We were having our regular meeting in Downham. A couple of men came in asking for our assistance to obtain better wages and for the price of flour to be fixed for poor families. They thought if we announced what we thought was fair, the local farmers and overseers would heed us.

'They came with a small party but a bigger crowd gathered while we were talking. When we announced our decision, two shillings wages and flour for poor families at two shillings and sixpence per stone, instead of the current rate of three shillings and nine pence, the men who asked for help were content but the crowd objected most violently. We went out to them to explain but they came at us with weapons, cudgels and the like, and we had to run for our lives.' He shakes his head, unwilling to continue, and gives way to Sir Thomas Hare.

'They followed us in, deliberately damaging doors and furniture. We barricaded ourselves and made away through the back but when the mob realised we had escaped, some took chase. I managed to get to Mr. Lemmon's, but Dering had to hide in a garden for hours before he reached safety at Mr. Saffrey's. The crowd was chanting his name and shouting they'd kill him.

It was terrifying. He needed a large brandy when he arrived, I can tell you.'

Mr. Lemmon adds 'Despite that, Mr. Dering had the presence of mind to get a message to the Upwell Yeomanry, but it was evening before they could get to Downham. By that time, the crowd had rampaged through the town, breaking into shops and public houses and demanding food and drink. Some were quite ruined by drink but they kept roaming about, goading each other on. The Yeomanry arrested two men, and the local constable locked several in the gaol. After that it became quiet, till next morning.'

Sir Thomas Hare takes up again. 'It seems both the men arrested were from Southery, not Downham, and people in Southery claimed they had not taken part in the disturbance. They marched from Southery to appeal for the men's release, gathering a crowd on the way. When they reached Downham there were hundreds of them. It was Dering who had to deal with them.'

Dering shakes his head, but continues. 'They wanted the two men released. Some had punt guns full of shot, some had old swords, they all had some sort of weapon. I agreed to the release, to avoid the bloodshed I feared if there was a violent confrontation. I assumed they would disperse, but instead they demanded all the men be released from gaol.

'The men were not criminals, no misdemeanour had been proved against them. They were only doing what every one of us would do in trying to provide food for their wives and children. So reluctantly, I agreed to that too. But still the crowd stayed in town. No business was done, townspeople feared to come onto the streets, and it had to stop.

'All I could do was to read the Riot Act and warn them if they didn't disperse, they would face the death penalty. The death penalty! How have events turned that it comes to me to threaten them with death? At any other time they'd be working peaceably in the fields! I am desolate that I could offer nothing else to relieve their problems.'

'You had no choice, Mr. Dering,' Mr. Lemmon offers quietly. 'You warned them. That is the law.'

'These people weren't agitators or conspirators against the state,' Dering exclaims. 'They were hungry and wanting jobs. When the Yeomanry advanced, they captured nineteen persons before the crowd dispersed, but thank God, they were well disciplined and nobody was injured. Now sixteen of our men and women are being carted off to Norwich. They're on trial for their lives, gentlemen, for their very lives, and it sickens me to the heart.'

It is a desperate event indeed. Despite several high level appeals for leniency, two are executed by hanging, five are transported to Australia, three of them for life and several are sentenced to hard labour.

'Perhaps if we could raise the funds to get the Cut started, there would be plentiful jobs for a considerable time,' Reverend Goode suggests. 'Would the Bedford Level Corporation provide a loan, do you think?'

'Mr. Dering, are you going to the next Bedford Level meeting? Might you be able to inquire with the Board?' Hoseason asks, and places a sympathetic hand on his shoulder as Dering nods.

A joint application for £30,000 from the Eau Brink Commissioners and the Corporation of the Bedford Level is delivered to the Chancellor of the Exchequer, but Whitehall rejects it as not expedient.

There is no option but to continue measures to obtain payments dating back eight years from King's Lynn Corporation, and recover taxes from other non-payers. By November, the King's Lynn Commissioners of Sewers have entered the dispute and actioned their legal power to formally require the Eau Brink Commissioners to answer a charge of not repairing the banks. The Eau Brink Commissioners plead Not Guilty, and determine to move the case to the King's Bench in London for a more considered judicial decision as soon as possible.

## The Lamb Inn, Ely
## May 1817

In response to an avalanche of petitions from around the country highlighting severe poverty, hunger and distress, a Poor Employment Bill is in progress through Parliament to issue Exchequer Bills for loans to finance public works and employment of the poor.

The Eau Brink Commissioners, now including Lord William Bentinck recently returned from his most recent post as diplomatic envoy to Italy, jump at the opportunity it presents to fund work on the Cut when the cost of labour is low. A joint application for £15,000 from the Eau Brink Commissioners and the Corporation of the Bedford Level is delivered to the Chancellor of the Exchequer.

By mid-June, the Earl of Hardwicke reports that the bid might not be eligible within the provisions of the Act. One of its requirements is that work should already have started on any project for which an application is made, and drainage projects are not included. It is already too late to change the Bill which was passed by the House of Commons on 23rd May as the Public Works Loans Act 1817.

Not to be easily defeated, all Eau Brink Commissioners and members of the Bedford Level Corporation who are also members of either the Commons or the Lords meet the following week at the House of Lords to address the Chancellor personally. An amendment to the Poor Employment Act is suggested, which is duly presented to the Commons on 24th June, being passed there by 4th July.

At the same time, the 1795 Eau Brink Act, which was originally limited to ten years and was subsequently revised for shorter periods, each with rising tax rates, is again approaching a need for renewal. The Commissioners resolve to apply for both a continuation and an enlargement of the Eau Brink Act to provide working finance. It requires a tax rise to one shilling an acre per annum for five years, a more than threefold increase on the basic rate of the original Act. Each revision enables the

Commissioners to classify land according to its value, with prime agricultural land being rated as multiples of the basic rate. Despite strong opposition from landowners whose harvests are stunted and a general agricultural slump diminishing their incomes, the enlarged Act is authorised.

# Part Four
# The Writing

# Part Four
# The Writing

As autumn approaches, Lord William Bentinck reveals that an issue of Exchequer Bills has been agreed for a loan of £15,000. John Rennie is appointed Engineer and given full supervision of the works, with power to spend and appoint. He asks Thomas Townshend, an engineer with whom he had worked on numerous projects in Fenland and Ireland, to set out the line of the Cut accurately and then to continue as Resident Engineer. His decision on all matters is to be final.

Rennie reviews the contested question of the optimum width of the diggings. Nearly a century previously, Nathaniel Kinderley had recommended 200 feet. Then Hyde Page and Mylne settled on 480. Huddart's judgement was 296. Rennie's instruction is for an average of 240 feet. By October, a working supervisory committee made up of twelve of the most active local Eau Brink Commissioners is appointed to give direction and supervise the expenditure. Thomas Hoseason takes a riverside house near Wiggenhall St. Germans opposite Eau Brink, more conveniently situated for a works base and to offer hospitality to visiting consultants, rather than his mansion at the farm he called Shetland which is six miles away.

Mr. Charles Burcham from Holt, surveyor and sometime Chamberlain of King's Lynn Corporation, is commissioned to draw a detailed map of the lands involved, together with information on the ownership of the plots. Soon, he is appointed Comptroller of the entire project to administer finances. Mr. Lemmon negotiates with the tenants to ask what they will accept to compensate for workmen entering their land, and to quit the area before next Lady Day at the end of March 1818.

Rennie recommends contractors Joliffe and Banks to build the Cut. He has worked with them on several large projects and their combination of effective completion of work with substantial financial backing is particularly helpful. The Eau Brink Commissioners agree to pay them in interest bearing securities for amounts exceeding £5,000 until finance is in place.

By June 1818 Joliffe and Banks have been paid over £5,000 of the £20,000 it will cost to excavate over 25,000 floors of earth, at thirteen shillings and nine pence per floor. One floor of earth is 324 cubic feet. One barrow holds approximately two and a half cubic feet of earth, meaning around three million barrows of earth will have to be removed to excavate the Eau Brink Cut.

## The River Great Ouse
## 1818

> *I tremble at the thud of metal studded boots striding closer, crocodiles in rough wool, seeking their prey with penetrating eyes. Tin cans rattle in bundles on their backs, and their sharpened spades, with bright edges snapping in the sun, lie in wait across their shoulders.*
>
> *They bring wagons with tents and tools, pickaxes, wheelbarrows and planks. They swarm over me like black ants fleeing from a nest and gather where tall carved posts are pushed into the fields.*
>
> *They stand with other men, talking, pointing. Carpenters and labourers are put to work building cabins and marking out where tents can be erected, finding tinder, fresh water and food. Opportunists bring their covered wagons, with every service essential to working men, whether they want it or not.*

Shopkeepers in town order for a bonanza, filling shelves with coarse warm clothes, waterproofs and underwear. Dressmakers too, with skirts, shawls and bonnets, for some bring their wives, children, brothers and nephews. The quick clever ones find shelter in houses in South Lynn or rooms in the villages. The slower, with bare survival in mind and iron in their muscles, settle for draughty barns and a shanty town within sight of mansions furnished with crystal and harps.

## Wiggenhall St. Germans
## Summer 1818

The landlord of the Three Tuns cooks pots of stew and lays in more barrels of ale, ready for the evening crowd. Men trickle in from dusk. Soon the benches are crammed full so they lean on the walls. Someone starts to play a fiddle, a lively tune that has feet tapping, and a tin whistle joins in. Then a red-faced man starts to sing, and the company is caught up in a chorus of popular song, ribald and none too complimentary to gentry folk. English, Irish, Scots, Welsh, they'd all known the dismal prospect of worklessness and hunger alongside plenty, and all are thankful to be done with the threat of it for a while.

Many dally with local girls, but they are frowned on in the camp, not for the morals, though there are plenty of older men who glower at the youths, but because there is no privacy to be had anywhere.

*The walking men set fires that glow long into darkness, holding out their hands for warmth and eating from tin pots. Every day they scratch more into my crust. They scrape off my fertile skin and gouge deep into my clay.*

*Strangers bring two barges groaning under heavy loads. Pullies lift great metal engines onto carts which they trundle to the precipice of the trench. They fit loose pieces together and light a fire in its belly. It belches steam and pumps water from holes the men dig. It thumps on, day and night.*

*Men descend lower to the right and left, shovelling, exposing. They throw each spade load into wheelbarrows. More men run the barrows up narrow planks to the surface, balanced like tightrope walkers made giant with muscle, on tiers of planks for mile after mile. A thousand barrows, a million, three million, more than there are stars above me.*

*They snatch my living creatures from their dark dens and dump them in monstrous heaps where the breath is squashed out of them. They steal my goodness, my soil of centuries, as they penetrate deeper, more than two men deep.*

*My earth weeps.*

*Still they dig far below me, below the bones of primitive creatures and tree trunks that stood proud before the great surge from the sea, when these men's far distant ancestors walked the land. They find no floor, only the hulls of boats whose owners ran for their lives in a swell of my waters. Some I took, because I desired them.*

*Among my marshes were secret paths known only to the wise people who lived in my margins. They drew salt from my banks and used my watery aisles to trade with others. They did no harm.*

*Then armies came. They built garrisons on my foreshores and palaces for their lords, but in time my mists made them cold and they faltered. I made them more like my people and now they are my people. Those men used me and tended me. Not like these scoundrels who have learned disrespect.*

*The pump sucks my tears, the very water that surrounds me, no matter how fast I help it seep back to salve my gashes.*

*They turn to my tributaries. They scour and clear their rubbish from my veins and they boast they are supreme. They sink fortunes into cutting me and they justify their squander by saying they have beaten the cursed river, oblivious to whose neglect caused my collapse.*

*I move their vessels but they slap me like a birthing child.*

*I nourish their fields with richness from the deeps but they think the golden crops are their own cleverness.*

*I am spent. I long for clouds to shade me, to soak me, to wash away the dust and the stink of their living.*

*Winter comes. The men leave me to heal my gouges. In the silence of snowfall the pump still thuds on, forever being fed coals.*

*The days grow longer, then the men return. I am rested, stronger now with my winter's rain. In the night, a force comes from the North sky to overwhelm them. I encourage the open sea to grow wild with massive waves that crash onto my beaches, bringing ships to strand on my marshes. Thunder drowns out the noise of the pump. Men run for high ground and solid walls, lit by sheets of lightening in a manic concert to their destruction.*

## The River Great Ouse
## 1820

*I am enshadowed. Axes cut great oaks from virgin forest in a foreign land. Their graceful branches are slashed and they are left prone, defenceless, to die of dryness. They are dragged through muck and rocks and stripped naked of their precious bark. Their fulsome roundness is hacked to sharp corners, the most abominable shape in the natural universe.*

*The trunks are hauled onto ships which sail to my shallows and are dumped like worthless tinder for men to smear with poisonous metallic paint. No matter now. They are already beyond life.*

*In the heat of summer when my tide is low, they are tipped on end and hammered into my bed like a chain of sores. Then men fix new branches to the uprights. They form arms outstretched to the sky but they are held with great metal bolts, unable to sway in a gentle breeze. They are eternally crucified.*

*Twelve times men do this, edging in two lines further away from the firm ground beyond South Lynn and the open fields of the west. Then they stretch planks along the lines and finally more planks across them, until men from each side can walk with dry boots to shake hands above me. This five eyed monster will forever hide the sun from me.*

*Still they are not satisfied. They hinge the central section so it can be raised if high masted ships need to pass on my water; oh yes, they want to use me still. A bridgekeeper tends it all, but he doesn't look at me below him, doesn't see I am slowed with a dozen boulders in my way. Only the old rivermen stand with clenched jaws, baffled and fearful for the livelihood of their sons.*

The Eau Brink Act stipulates that roads must connect the bridge with existing routes. A road is required from South Lynn to the foot of the new bridge, and on the other side from West Lynn, stretching further to a strategic westerly point across what would become the old course of the river.

With the entire project funded by the Exchequer Bill Loan, the Eau Brink Commissioners look no further than the engineer Thomas Telford, expert on roads and an Exchequer Loan Commissioner, to advise Banks and Jessop on its construction, in particular over the drained river bed. For good measure, John McAdam is consulted. They advocate stone with a precise size in several layers which allows good draining and resistance to frost damage. McAdam uses a further top layer of smaller stones, which are not damaged by metal carriage wheels so much as larger stones.

A crooked road which turns sharp south west from the bridge is agreed. It follows the bank of the Eau Brink Cut for about one and a half miles until it crosses the Tilney All Saints parish boundary which passes to the north, then turns west at the Eau Brink Bank, and north again across the old course of the river to a point slightly east of Islington Hall close to the Shore Boat Inn on the far bank of the river. There it joins an existing road bending east to Tilney.

To complement this, the Paving Commissioners, a group of local gentry including Anthony Hamond of West Acre, lay a new road from South Gates straight into town.

## King's Lynn
## Tuesday, 28th June 1821

It is a perfect summer day. Bakers are busy from an early hour selling mountains of bread rolls and buns. Confectioners bring candies to tempt every palette and toffee apples to make even sour fruit luscious. Carts park by the open spaces, with elderflower and fruit cordials, fresh strawberries, cherries and rhubarb, and every variety of seafood. For just a few pennies every citizen can have a banquet. By midday, great crowds are gathered along the processional route to the new Marshland Freebridge.

The gentry assemble by the Walks. Their carriages are festooned with ribbons and flowers, with their horses to match. The band strikes up at one o'clock leading the procession straight down the newly paved London Road and on through the South Gates.

Thomas Hoseason leads off, followed by Sir Thomas Hare and Anthony Hamond. Following them, Mayor Scarlet Everard and members of the Corporation, the engineers John Rennie, Thomas Telford and Thomas Townshend, and Charles Burcham who orchestrates the entire event. All manner of commercial coaches including the new Lynn and London coach, pulled by four fine bay horses, and scores of private carriages line up behind them.

Children run alongside waving flags and banging anything they can find to make a noise. Along the bank then, to the bridge itself. It is draped with national flags hanging against a hazy sky. A central banner proclaims 'Prosperity to the Eau Brink Drainage and Durability to the Marshland Free Bridge', proud against a white balustrade assuring the bridge's strength and safety for all travellers. Below, vessels fly the colours of the nations and trading partners from every corner of the globe.

At the foot of the bridge, men who had worked on it run towards Hoseason's carriage. They unhitch his horses then pull his carriage across themselves, with much cheering. As Hoseason arrives on the West Lynn side, cannons are fired and the band plays 'See the Conquering Hero Comes'.

Thousands of pedestrians follow the carriages but long before all the walkers cross, Hoseason gives a speech of thanks to all involved.

Then over 200 people take lunch, paid for by the directors. Booths ply refreshments for the walkers and the workmen dine on a sheep roasted on an open spit with barrels of beer to toast a successful venture. The crowds walk back and forth, just for the novelty. As evening approaches, merry fiddle tunes invite them to dance on the bridge.

Later, as guests of Joliffe and Banks, the gentry dine at Mr. Thorpe's Coffee House known as the Freemasons Tavern, on the junction of the High Street and Surrey Street, and celebrations continue well into the night.

## King's Lynn
## Tuesday, 24th July 1821

*I am woken by the screech of high pitched reeds and the shrill notes of a trumpet. Drums rattle time. Men stride sure footed on the slats above me. The tramp of feet and the clatter of hooves gnaw at my tranquillity. The moon comes closer to inspect my discomfort and my breeze responds, becoming hard by North West.*

*On the third day the tide comes full strength against the dam built to prevent my waters drowning their workings. From dawn, men watch my waters rise. They send riders upriver to open Denver Sluice and they pull men out of the diggings as they see their dam start to crumble.*

*A tiny trickle expands weak rat burrows. The vermin sense danger and hundreds scamper away down dark tunnels on the banks.*

*Soon a cascade falls from the dam. It pulls earth from its body and then the wall is a sieve, a violent waterfall that swirls into the diggings, racing, tumbling over itself in a brown foaming torrent of silt and rock.*

*The wave speeds along, pushing the summer waters aside. Men in unmoored barges fight to stay afloat, clinging to riverside dolphin posts but being dragged dangerously sideways and smashing into each other. At Denver Sluice, the greatest force of my tidal waters escapes down the One Hundred Foot River, sparing the destruction of my old banks, but my ripples damage landings as far as the River Cam.*

**Lynn Roads**
**Sunday, 29th July 1821**

The Swiftsure, recently commissioned as a passenger steam barge on the Thames, chugs to its anchorage in the Lynn Roads. Enormous paddle wheels on each side whisk up a trail of foaming bubbles that float like a bride's lace veil across the estuary. The vessel has a mast but its sails remained furled, redundant on this fine evening. Its yellow and brown hull glows in the evening sun, and smoke whispers from its tulip shaped chimney atop a red and white funnel.

This is the Swiftsure's first venture onto coastal waters. Its voyage from London Bridge is ambitious for a boat designed for river journeys. Sir Joseph Sidney Yorke, retired Lord of the Admiralty, is on board to report its progress to the Navy and to represent his half-brother the Earl of Hardwicke.

Thomas Hoseason hosts the passengers from London. It takes around thirty hours to reach the Wash where other Eau Brink Commissioners join them. They stand on the prow, each drinking in the anticipation of the next few days in the company of other enterprising men. Their acquaintance with the engineers of this venture leads them to believe steam powered engines that can propel ships at speed over such distances could also pull carriages on metal rails. They are already looking for the next good investment, now that interest in canals has passed its peak.

**King's Lynn**
**Tuesday, 31st July 1821**

Dawn strengthens to an intense blue sky. A gentle breeze freshens the day, barely rustling the yellowing corn in the fields opposite as Charles Brown leaves home. He is buoyed by success finally emerging from the years of frustration. He senses a lasting achievement in his little corner of England, so far from the capricious sophistication of the capitals of Europe, but with its own distinctive rewards. Here are such generous skies, such a bounteous world, offered to those who pause to look at them on this glorious morning.

His carriage turns along part of the new road to the bridge, passing villagers on foot heading for the ferry. For them, there was little to be gained from the extra distance to the bridge when they could wait in sunshine at West Lynn and arrive more quickly into the centre of Lynn's riverside.

Brown has travelled the world. He has been astounded by the confidences told him by some whose word could change the lives of millions, yet today he tingles with delight as his carriage rumbles over the bridge. His horses' hooves sound a smart staccato rhythm on its planks. No more irritating delays, no more anxiety around the ever changing tides and unpredictable power of the waters.

He wishes Mary was by his side, so she would know he has resolved the desperate torment she experienced whenever crossing this river was likely. After the ferry sank, she insisted on taking the long detour every time they went into Lynn but she has lain in the churchyard these nine years back. The Cut holds potential to mend Brown's finances, but this bridge, his bridge, he thinks, is his victory.

High tide is due at eight o'clock. People gather along the banks to watch the Swiftsure sail into the harbour. They are amazed to see a ship move so quickly, with its coloured flags fluttering and clouds of white-grey smoke billowing from its chimney into a clear azure sky. The spectacle surpasses all imaginings. In about half an hour, Swiftsure covers the nine miles from the deep water of the Lynn Roads and moors safely at the Common Staithe.

The caterers have installed their provisions and the Band is tuned up. Dignitaries are guided through the throng of townspeople and board the ship. Some walk together from the Duke's Head Hotel ready for the early start. Locals and their guests arrive in carriages from private houses out of town.

The ferry is in constant transit with sightseers who press along the quays while hundreds stand on the West Lynn banks. As the eighth hour approaches, every vantage point is taken. Windows and balconies bulge with expectant onlookers. Young men and boys balance on walls and low roofs while others pull wagons to the riverside and perch precariously on top. This is a sight not to be missed.

Some, still mounted or in small carriages, mingle on the banks clear of the town. Bets are laid. Who can outrun the barge? Will any rider get to Wiggenhall alongside the Swiftsure? Plenty think so.

A gun fires. The bridge is raised, and the Swiftsure moves away from Common Staithe as the band plays 'God Save the King'. A flotilla of small boats, decked out with flags and bunting turn upriver, ready to follow in Swiftsure's slipstream, but few can keep up.

As the steam boat passes through the bridge, a band nearby plays 'Rule Britannia' and a man dressed like Neptune with his trident leaps into the river. He calls for a toast to the Wooden Walls of Old England in homage to the great Admirals who routed the French. A noisy yell of approval comes from everybody on the bridge. On from there, a tangle of wagons, carriages and horses career along the bank, their riders whooping excitedly in their efforts to beat the steam boat and win their wagers.

The Swiftsure returns without delay. Its captain is anxious to return to deeper waters, for damage to its paddles through catching on the top of hidden shoals as the tide falls is too perilous to risk. He'll be back tomorrow for the ladies, who will extend their trip out to the estuary. The river is calm, glittering in the sharp summer light as it stands ready to return to the sea.

The River Great Ouse had a beauty that morning. It flowed obediently in the fresh breeze, lending its empowerment, but few who knew it were beguiled by its apparent benevolence. This new manicured river and its acceptance of the chugging demon dividing its waters might well spit a judgement come winter.

## The River Great Ouse, King's Lynn
## 1822

*I am choking ...*

# Epilogue

Sir Thomas Hyde Page died on 30th June 1821 aged 75, just two days after the bridge opened and a month before the official opening of the Eau Brink Cut. He was the last surviving participant of Lord Townshend's 1775 attempt to divert the River Great Ouse.

Lord Townshend had died 14th September 1807 aged 83, and Robert Mylne on 5th May 1811 aged 77, leaving his son William Chadwell Mylne as Chief Engineer for the New River Company and several projects in the Fens.

John Rennie died on 4th October 1821 aged 60, and Sir Martin Browne Folkes on 11th December 1821 aged 72. None of them saw Hyde Page's prediction come to pass that narrowing the dimensions of the river would lead to severe silting.

Although there was an initial improvement, flow through the Cut by 1823 proved to be insufficient and silting in King's Lynn harbour continued to worsen. In 1825, Thomas Telford recommended that the new channel should be widened at an extra cost of £33,000. This eased navigation but did little to solve problems in the estuary or drainage. John Rennie's son John, later knighted, was asked to re-design Denver Sluice in 1834.

The road from the Freebridge at King's Lynn across Marshland to Walpole Cross Keys and the River Nene was extended in 1831 by the Cross Keys Bridge at Sutton Bridge. It connected to roads through Lincolnshire giving improved road access to the northern counties.

The Grand Junction Canal opened a cheaper route for coal than the coast and river route. River Great Ouse deliveries of coal had halved by 1820. Railways reached King's Lynn by 1845 and took over transport of coal and goods. Navigation on the River Great Ouse was declared derelict by 1870. Recently, some parts have been restored for leisure pursuits.

A direct northerly outfall of the River Great Ouse was completed by the Norfolk Estuary Company in 1853. This diverted the River Great Ouse away from the shallow easterly bend around King's Lynn and its seaward approach, providing instead a deep channel from the harbour to the Wash across North Lynn, which is now reclaimed land on the eastern side of the river.

King's Lynn Docks and Railway Company built the Alexandra Dock with a railway junction in 1869. By 1876 over 500 ships were using the new dock each year. The larger Bentinck Dock opened in 1883. The port now handles around half a million tonnes each year which is transported by road.

Prompted by major flooding in 1937 and 1947, a Great Ouse Flood Protection Scheme was approved in 1949. At a cost of ten and a half million pounds it consisted of a relief channel parallel with the Great Ouse from Denver to Saddlebow near South Lynn. A new channel to carry the headwaters of the Rivers Wissey, Lark and Little Ouse to join the Great Ouse near Denver Sluice was completed in 1964.

The 1953 East Coast tidal surge killed fifteen people and over one and a half thousand were evacuated from South Lynn. In 1978 an even greater surge of hundreds of thousands of gallons of sea water created great distress and damaged property estimated at five and a half million pounds. A defence scheme began in 1981 which included one and a half kilometres of concrete surge wall, four outfall structures across the old fleets and tidal creek, replacement of the Alexander Dock gates, and fifty three flood gates. The existing river banks were strengthened to provide a one in a hundred year standard of risk protection.

When the Environment Agency warns of dangerously high water levels, the National Rivers Authority closes all flood gates in co-operation with police, local authorities and the dock master.

A fifth of the area of East Anglia is below high tide level. A pumping station to support drainage and flood defence was built at Wiggenhall St. Germans in 1934. Its replacement was opened in 2011 by Lord James Russell, brother of the 15th Duke of Bedford. Costing thirty eight million pounds, it has six pumps that can move one hundred tonnes of water a second to manage a one in a hundred year rainfall event, allowing for predicted climate changes until 2050. Its elver pass gives access for eels into the Middle Level rivers and drains to restore the eel population which has fallen to critical levels.

Around twelve percent of the UK is peatland which in its natural state binds carbon dioxide. When drained for arable or other human uses it becomes a source of carbon dioxide, methane and nitrous oxide. Significant research is taking place on the contribution of shrinking peatlands to greenhouse gas emissions and global warming, to inform decisions on future management, food security, economics and global sustainability.

If William Elstobb were still here, he would be in a paradise of precise numbers. Looking back, he might realise that the sporadic surges of man's efforts to reduce flooding from the river coincide with phases of wetter climate. Meteorologists and environmentalists now recognise global climate change is responsible for steeper trends in rising sea levels, drier hotter summers, sudden heavy rainfalls and shifting coastlines which raise the spectre of frequent extremes of drought and flood in the future.

*My waters have been controlled temporarily by human ingenuity. I flow on, quietly waiting for the time I will be heard again.*

# Ripples

**Henry Bell** (1748-1820) of Wallington Hall, near Downham Market was an Alderman of King's Lynn from 1789-1820 and Mayor in 1789/90. He married Elizabeth Browne, heir of Scarlet Browne, sometime Alderman then Town Clerk of King's Lynn. Henry Bell descended from Sir Robert Bell, Recorder of Lynn and its MP in 1562, who rose to become Speaker of the House of Commons and Chief Baron of the Exchequer in 1576, and died in 1578. Sir Robert married Dorothy Beaupré, daughter of Edmund of Beaupré Hall, Outwell. Dorothy's second marriage in 1579 was to Sir John Peyton, originally from the Norfolk-Suffolk border, who became Governor of Jersey. He was granted the manor of Doddington, Cambridgeshire which at 37,000 acres was one of the largest parishes in England, lodged between Wisbech and Chatteris as a reward for his services which included being Lieutenant of the Tower of London when Sir Walter Raleigh was held prisoner there.

Beaupré Hall descended to Francis Bell (1626-1680) who married Dorothy Oxburgh of Hagbeach Hall, Emneth. Their children included Beaupré Bell who left Beaupré Hall to his sister Dorothy who married William Greaves of Fulborne, Cambs. This William Beaupré Bell Greaves died in 1785, leaving his estates at Fulborne and Beaupré Hall to his great nephew Richard Greaves Townley (1786-1855), originally from Lancashire.

Philip Bell, grandson of Robert, was successively Governor of Bermuda, Providence Island and Barbados. He died in 1678 and left his Wallington estate to his nephew Phillip Bell. This Philip Bell had married Anne Peyton, daughter of Sir Algernon Peyton of Doddington, and distant relatives of Charles Nalson Cole. They were the grandparents of Henry Bell of Wallington, Mayor of Lynn in 1789. This Henry Bell should not be mistaken for Henry Bell, merchant of Kings Lynn, Mayor 1678 and 1670, or his son Henry Bell the architect, who were descended from a Yorkshire family.

**The Bentinck family** were diplomats, soldiers and politicians from the Netherlands. Hans Willem Bentinck (1649-1709) was in the service of William, Prince of Orange for whom Bentinck negotiated the Prince's marriage to Princess Mary, heir of King James II in 1677. He was significant in the political and practical aspects of the accession to the British throne of William and Mary in 1689 when he was rewarded by being raised to Earl of Portland and received estates including Terrington St. Clement, Welbeck Abbey in Nottinghamshire and Bulstrode Park in Buckinghamshire.

He married twice, providing descendants from both marriages who were successful diplomats and military men. From his first marriage in 1678 to Anne Villiers, lady-in-waiting to the Queen, a line descended which included the 3rd Duke of Portland (1738-1809) twice Prime Minister of Britain and his son Lord William Bentinck, Governor of Madras 1803-1806 and Governor General of India 1828-1835. Lord William Bentinck was MP for Nottinghamshire several times including 1816-1826 during negotiations for the Eau Brink Cut, and MP for King's Lynn 1826-1828.

Hans Willem's second marriage in 1700 to Jane Temple (1672-1751) brought son William Bentinck, 1st Count Bentinck (1704-1774) who married Charlotte Sophie, Countess von Aldenburg (1715-1800), a distant cousin of the Russian Empress Catherine the Great. Their two sons were Christian (1734-1768), Count de Rhoon, and Royal Navy Captain John Albert Bentinck, of Terrington St. Clement (1737-1775). John Albert was an inventor whose Cole-Bentinck pump became standard issue for Royal Navy ships. His enclosure of the coastal margins of his estate resulted in contracting 'Fen Fever', a type of malaria, from which he died. His children with Renira van Tuyll van Serooskerken included Vice-Admiral William Bentinck (1764-1813) who also had a distinguished naval and diplomatic career.

**Dr. Sir Charles Brown,** (died 1827) physician. Charles Brown's early life is obscure. For some years he was a physician in Carmarthen, Wales before travelling to Krichev, Russia in 1783 where he worked with Samuel Bentham, a mechanical engineer and brother of Jeremy Bentham, the philosopher. Brown became Medical Director to the Russian Army, numbering the family of Empress Catherine the Great among his patients. He became physician to King William Frederick III of Prussia who raised him to a Knight of the Prussian Order of the Red Eagle in 1816 and he became a Knight of Great Britain in 1818. His finances remained difficult and he was buried at Clenchwarton.

There were several unrelated **Brown families** with interests in Marshland at the time of the Eau Brink Cut. Besides Dr. Sir Charles Brown, (not to be confused with Mr. Charles Brown of nearby Tilney St. Lawrence who died in 1823), the 1819 Eau Brink map by Charles

Burcham shows the other major landowners included Sir Martin Browne Folkes of Hillington, King's Lynn and Mrs Hester Brown. She presented a petition against the Eau Brink Cut to the House of Lords in April 1818 where she is identified as the widow of Edward Candler Brown. He had inherited land from Margaret Cecil, wife of Sir Robert Brown of Wiggenhall St. Mary, MP for Ilchester who died in 1760. Margaret was descended from William Cecil, 1st Baron Burghley. Edward Candler also inherited from his father's family who were senior lawyers in Ireland. Edward married Hester, daughter of Phineus Bury of Cork. They took the name Brown as a condition of inheritance, and lived in Dublin and Somerset.

**Sir Martin Browne Folkes** (1749-1821) was the son of barrister William Folkes of Hillington, King's Lynn and Mary, daughter of Dr. Sir William Browne (1692-1774), a physician in King's Lynn for more than thirty years and President of the College of Physicians. Martin Folkes, President of the Royal Society, was his uncle. On the death of both his father and grandfather, he took the name Browne Folkes. In 1775 he married Fanny, daughter of Sir John Turner of Warham, whose family had represented King's Lynn in Parliament for over forty years and were connected by marriage to Sir Robert Walpole, Britain's first 'Prime Minister'.

**Charles Nalson Cole** (1723-1804) lawyer and legal antiquary, was born in North Crawley, Buckinghamshire, the son of Rev. Charles Cole and Mary Williams. His paternal grandfather was William Cole, apothecary of Ely. His maternal grandmother was Elizabeth Nalson, daughter of Rev. Dr. John Nalson (1637-1685) Rector of Doddington, Cambs. and Alice Peyton, the daughter of Rev. Algernon Peyton who succeeded to the manor of Doddington in 1659. Elizabeth Nalson married Phillip Williams, who succeeded John Nalson as Rector of Doddington. Charles Nalson Cole was Registrar and Auditor of the Bedford Level Corporation 1757-1804. He summarised numerous reports for the Board in clear and non-technical language which was sometimes highly critical. He published "A Collection of Laws which form the Constitution of the Bedford Level Corporation, with an introductory history thereof," in 1761, and in 1762 produced a new edition of Sir William Dugdale's "History of embanking and drayning of divers fenns and marshes, &c." Mr. Cole was also a personal friend of Soame Jenyns, who at his death in 1787 bequeathed to Cole the copy-right of all his works, with a request for Cole to superintend their posthumous publication.

**Thomas Cubit** (born about 1759) entered the Military Academy at Woolwich in September 1776 aged about 16, and graduated as a practitioner engineer in what was to become the Royal Corps of Engineers. He resigned in May 1791 having served for 15 years. Thomas Cubit assisted Thomas Hyde Page's survey of 1775, along with three other cadets from the Drawing Office in the Tower of London, which evolved into the Ordnance Survey. His origin among the very numerous Thomas Cubitts (variable transcriptions) of North Norfolk remains obscure, as does his life after 1802. His more famous namesake Thomas Cubitt (1788-1855) was the son of Jonathan Cubitt, carpenter and millwright of Buxton, near Norwich. This Thomas, son of Jonathan, was the largest building contractor of the time in London. His brother William Cubitt (1791–1863) became Lord Mayor of London. Jonathan Cubitt of Buxton had a brother named Thomas whose date of birth must have been close to 1759, and may have been Thomas Cubit of the River Great Ouse, military engineer and surveyor.

**Sir Andrew Snape Hamond,** (1738-1828) was born in Blackheath, London, the only son of Robert Hamond and Susannah Snape, daughter of Robert Snape of Limekilns, Blackheath. Robert Hamond was a successful London merchant shipbroker, son of Samuel Hamond, carpenter and shipbroker of Wisbech, Cambs. There have been Hamond families around Wisbech since at least the 15th century. Andrew Snape Hamond joined the Royal Navy at fifteen and served with merit in the Seven Years' War. During the American Revolutionary War, he was Captain of HMS Roebuck of 44 guns for which he was knighted in 1778. He married twice, first to Cecilia Sutherland and second in 1779 to Anne, daughter of Major Henry Graeme of Middlesex and Perthshire, of the Graeme family of Braco, Scotland. Henry Graeme was Lieutenant-Governor of the island of St. Helena where he died in 1785.

Andrew Snape Hamond was briefly Lieutenant-Governor of Nova Scotia from 1781, and was created Baronet of Holly Grove, Windsor, in 1783. From 1785 to 1788 he was Commander-in-Chief of the Nore, including the River Medway and key naval bases around the Thames estuary. In 1792 he sat on the court-martial following the mutiny aboard Captain Bligh's HMS Bounty. By 1793 he was a Commissioner of the Navy Board and became its Comptroller for a further twelve years. From 1796, Andrew Snape Hamond was MP for Ipswich and one of the eleven ruling Brethren of Trinity House. He was elected a Fellow of the Royal Society in 1797, recommended by engineer Joseph Huddart, Neville Maskelyne, the Astronomer Royal and William Marsden, Secretary to the Admiralty. He resigned from Parliament and the Navy in 1806 with a pension of £1,500 p.a. and retired to his grand mansion, Hamond Lodge, at Terrington St. Clement where he died on 12th October 1828.

**Thomas Hoseason** (about 1765-1835) from Lerwick, in the Shetland Islands, built a house with seven guest bedrooms between Clenchwarton village and the coastal marsh bank, which he called Shetland Farm, now demolished. A public house nearby was called The Shetland Pony. In 1820, Hoseason also occupied a smaller house on the bank of the River Great Ouse opposite Eau Brink. The purchases coincided with an extended agricultural recession, leading to serious financial distress in Marshland. Thomas, deeply indebted, returned to India as a magistrate under the by then Governor-General, Lord William Bentinck. Angelica, his wife, remained in England with their younger children, but died shortly afterwards. Thomas Hoseason died of dysentery eight months later in Calcutta while his younger children were on voyage to join him there.

**Joseph Huddart** (1741-1816) inventor, mathematician and surveyor was born in Cumbria, and while young took command of his father's fleet of fishing vessels involved in the white fish trade. He progressed to the transatlantic trade where he worked on improving marine charts, including from 1771-1778 the waters of major marine channels for the East India Co. fleet. He turned to marine surveying in Great Britain and became an Elder of Trinity House. In 1793 he took out a patent for a new method of manufacturing rope which was more robust than previous methods. From 1800, Huddart worked with prestigious engineers including John Rennie in Ireland and Robert Mylne in Portsmouth. He experimented in optics, clock making and ship design and was considered to be a man of great integrity.

**The Jenyns family** interest in drainage starts with Sir John Jenyns (1596-1642) who was a Commissioner of Sewers in Somerset in 1625. His descendant Roger Jenyns was a Bedford Level Conservator by

1664. Roger's son John Jenyns of Hayes, (c.1660-1717) was MP for Cambridgeshire 1710-1717, and he succeeded his father as Surveyor General of the Bedford Level Corporation in 1693. His brother Sir Roger (1663-1740) acquired Bottisham Hall. Sir Roger's children by his second wife, Elizabeth Soame, included Soame Jenyns (1704-1787) writer, MP for Cambridgeshire, Lord of Trade 1755-1780 and Bailiff of the Bedford Level Corporation from 1769.

The Bottisham estate and a significant fortune passed to Rev. George Leonard Jenyns (1763-1848), a Canon of Ely Cathedral, Vicar of Swaffham Prior, and for many years the Chairman of the Bedford Level Corporation. He became an Eau Brink Commissioner in January 1800. He was succeeded by his son Rev. Leonard Jenyns (1800-1893), Vicar of Swaffham Bulbeck and curate of West Dereham, who married Jane, daughter of Rev. E. Daubeny.

Leonard Jenyns was a noted writer and natural scientist. He took the name Blomefield on receiving an inheritance in 1871 from Francis Blomefield, a distant cousin who was descended from Francis Blomefield, antiquary and compiler of 'A History of Norfolk'. One of Leonard's sisters was Harriet, married to Rev. John Henslow, Professor of Botany at Cambridge and Rector of Hitcham, Suffolk under whom Leonard studied along with fellow student Charles Darwin. Leonard was first choice for the naturalist on HMS Beagle, but turned down the offer due to ill health and parish duties. He suggested Charles Darwin as his replacement. Leonard Jenyns was a founding member of the Zoological Society. He set up the Cambridge Societies Museum, now the Cambridge University Museum of Zoology and numerous other bodies related to natural science.

**King's Lynn Corporation** was composed of Freemen who had completed an apprenticeship, or who were the oldest sons of Freemen. The status was occasionally purchased, or conferred on people who had rendered a particular service to the town such as Sir Thomas Hyde Page. Freemen were exempt from some port charges and were eligible to be elected to the Corporation by existing members of the Corporation.

During the years of negotiations on the Eau Brink Cut, the Corporation was dominated by merchant families whose brewing, coal and timber import businesses had centred in Lynn for many years. Marriages between these families were common. They included four generations of the Everard family, coal and wine importers who eventually moved into banking, the Bagges and Allens who were brewers owning numerous public houses, the Hogges coal importers, the Elsdens, originally wool merchants and the Self family who traded in timber. The Municipal Corporations Act in 1835 required self-electing boroughs such as King's Lynn to reform into town councils that were elected by ratepayers from representative wards. The merchants ruled no more.

**Robert Mylne** (1734–1811) Besides the Eau Brink Cut, his activities in Fenland included consultation on several bridges across the River Great Ouse in Downham Market and Wisbech, Carrow Road Bridge in Norwich and the bridge at Great Yarmouth.

His opinion was sought on Norwich Waterworks in 1789, and he designed several houses around Norwich. One of Mylne's most notable works was to design and install the sarcophagus for Admiral Nelson's tomb in St Paul's Cathedral, for which he was Surveyor from 1776. Mylne acquired a reputation as a difficult man to work with because of his insistence on precise detail and a conviction that he was always right. However, many of his achievements remain today. He was buried in the crypt of St. Paul's Cathedral.

**Sir Thomas Hyde Page** (1746–1821) was born in Harley Street, London, the son of Robert Hyde Page (d. 1764), also a military engineer, and Elizabeth, daughter of Francis Morewood. His studies at the Royal Military Academy, Woolwich, won a gold medal from King George III. He commanded the Royal Engineers of the Eastern coastal district and supervised the refurbishment of bases including Landguard Fort, Suffolk. In 1780, he organized the Dover Volunteers and was knighted in 1783. He transferred to the Invalid Engineers but his expertise remained in demand and he became chief consulting engineer of the port of Dublin, and other large scale projects in Ireland.

**John Watté** (Active 1769-1799) was a surveyor for several Fen landowners including the Duke of Bedford. He lived at Leverington, near Wisbech from 1770-1783, where he was also schoolmaster. He was an astronomer and Honorary Member of the Society of Civil Engineers 1795. His Fenland works included a survey of the old channel at the south end of Kimberley's Cut for the Bedford Level Corporation in 1777 and the Nene Estuary in the parishes of Newton, Tydd St. Mary and Tydd St. Giles. He added a new section to Elstobb's

1767 work on the River Nene from Peterborough to Eye in 1783 and worked with Golborne on the Wisbech Canal, completed in 1796. He also surveyed various areas of Norfolk in connection with enclosure awards.

**Philip Yorke, 3rd Earl of Hardwicke** (1757-1834) was the eldest son of Charles Yorke, the Lord Chancellor. He succeeded to his Uncle Philip's earldom and estates including Wimpole Hall. He was Lord Lieutenant of Cambridgeshire from 1790, MP for Cambridge 1780-1790, a member of the Privy Council in 1801, Knight of the Garter in 1803, and Lord Lieutenant of Ireland 1801-1805. In 1782 Philip 3rd Earl of Hardwicke married Elizabeth, sister of Rt. Hon. Rev. Charles Lindsay (1760-1846), Vicar of Wisbech St. Peter and St. Paul from 1787-1795. Hardwicke was Lord Lieutenant of Ireland when Lindsay became Bishop of Kildare, Ireland, and Dean of Christ Church, Dublin.

Hardwicke's association with the Plumptre family was through Rev. Joseph Plumptre's father, Rev. Robert, and uncle, Rev. Charles who were both Rectors of Wimpole. **Rev. Joseph Plumptre** (1758-1810), Vicar of St James, Newton in the Isle, was also domestic chaplain to Jemima, wife of Philip Yorke, 2nd Earl Hardwicke. **Rev. Thomas Sheepshanks** (1754-1818), Curate at Newton in the Isle, was Rector of Wimpole and domestic chaplain to Philip, 3rd Earl of Hardwicke from 1794-1818. He was the son of a prosperous Yorkshire yeoman farmer. He married Elizabeth Garland of Wisbech who died in 1782 and is buried at Walsoken, then Martha, daughter of Robert Gynn, of Wisbech.

# Sources

British Library including the Digital Collection.
British Library English Short Title Catalogue.
British History Online.
Cambridgeshire Archives Service.
Cambridgeshire Libraries.
Clergy of the Church of England Database.
History of Parliament Online.
Journals of the House of Commons and House of Lords.
Norfolk Libraries.
Norfolk Museums Service.
Norfolk Record Office including King's Lynn Borough Archives.
Newspapers: National, Norwich, Bury St. Edmunds and Cambridge.
The National Archives.
The Royal Society: Directory of Past Fellows.
Three Decks: Warships in the Age of Sail.
University of Nottingham Library Portland (Welbeck) Collection.
Parish Births, Marriages and Death records, Apprenticeship Records
and Westminster Rate Books, with genealogical and heraldic
directories, supported by family history websites.
Digitised libraries including: Early English Books Online Text
Creation Partnership, Ebooksread.com, Google Books, Haithi Trust
Digital Library, Heritage Books, Internet Archive, Project Gutenburg.

## Engineering Reports, Petitions and Pamphlets

Bedford Level Corporation and Eau Brink Commissioners. Minutes
of meetings. Cambridgeshire Archives Service.

Burcham, Charles. (1819). Map of the River Ouse with proposed
New Bridge and Eau Brink River. Norfolk Record Office.

Cole, Charles Nalson. (1784). Extracts from the Report of a View of
the South Level, Part of the Great Level of the Fenns, Called Bedford
Level; Summer of the Year 1777. Google Books.

Cooper, Charles H. (1842). Cambridge Corporation Petition as to
Navigation, 4th February 1777. Annals of Cambridge, Vol. 4, p. 385.

Elstobb, William. (1776). Observations on an Address to the Public,
dated 20th April, 1775, Superscribed Bedford Level, and Sign'd
Charles Nalson Cole, and on a Plan, and Draft of a Bill, Intended

to be Presented to Parliament, for Preserving the Drainage of the Middle and South Levels, and for Imposing Taxes on the Free Lands in the Said Levels. Google Books.

Golborne, James. (1791). The report of James Golborne of the city of Ely, Engineer, in pursuance of several resolutions passed by a committee of land owners and others interested in the improvement of the outfall of the River Ouse. Google Books.

Golborne, J. (1777). The Report of Mr. J(ohn). G. on a view taken of the Middle and South [Bedford] Levels, and their outfalls to sea; with a plan for draining the said Levels. Google Books.

Hodskinson, J. (1793). The report of Joseph Hodskinson engineer, on the probable effect which a new cut, now in contemplation from Eau-Brink to a little above Lynn, will have on the harbour and navigation of Lynn; with a plan for improving the present channel, both above and below the town. British Library Digital Collection.

Huddart, Capt. J. (1804). Eau Brink New River, or Cut. Deed poll, stating the opinion (in the nature of an award). In pursuance of the reference to him by Sir Thomas Hyde Page, and Robert Mylne. Cambridgeshire Archives Service.

Hudson, John. (1792). On the probable effect the proposed Cut from Eau-Brink to Lynn will have on the banks and drainage of the Bedford South Level. British Library Digital Collection.

An Impartial Proprietor. (1777). Observations on the Means of Better Draining the Middle and South Level of the Fenns by Two Gentlemen who have taken a View Thereof. including The report and opinion of James Creassy respecting the drainage of the Middle and South Levels of the Fenns Called the Bedford-Levels, 1777, and Thomas Hyde Page's report to the Bedford Level Corporation, 1777. Bedfordshire Archive Service. Russell Collection, Fens Box 1, bundle 2.

Jenyns, Soame. (Attributed to) (1777). Remarks on a Bill Presented to Parliament in the Last Sessions, Intituled, A Bill For Preserving the Drainage of the Middle and South Levels, and the Several Navigations Through the Same, &c. Google Books.

Kinderley Jr. Nathaniel. (1751). The Ancient and Present State of the Navigation of the Towns of Lyn, Wisbech, Spalding and Boston. A revision of his father Nathaniel's plan published anonymously in 1721. Google Books.

Member of the Committee. (1794). Reported in: A few short observations upon a pamphlet intituled A View of the Conduct of the Parties respecting the Proposal of Accommodation offered by Merchants of Lynn to the Promoters of the Eau-Brink Cut. British Library Digital Collection.

Mutton, Norman. (1967). The Use of Steam Drainage in the making of the Eau Brink Cut quoting letters between John Towers Allen and James Watt in December 1782. Industrial Archaeology, Vol. 4, No. 4.

Nickalls, Joseph. (1793). Report upon the consequences which the New Cut, from Eau Brink, would be attended with to drainage, navigation, the harbour and town of Lynn. Google Books.

Page, Thomas Hyde. (1775). The Reports or Observations of Sir Thomas Hyde Page, on the Means of Draining the South and Middle Levels of the Fens. Google Books.

Page, Thomas Hyde. (1794). Minutes of the Evidence of Sir Thomas Hyde Page, Knight, on the Second Reading of the Eau Brink Drainage Bill. Google Books.

Page, Thomas Hyde. (1794). Estimate of the Expense of Carrying into execution the plan of Embankment recommended by Sir Thomas Hyde Page for the improvement of the Drainage of the South and Middle Levels. Google Books.

Page, T.H. & Mylne, R. (1802). Correspondence upon the subject of the Eau Brink Cut between Sir Thomas Hyde Page and Mr. Mylne, in the years 1801 and 1802. Bedford Level Corporation. Google Books.

Parliament of Great Britain. (1795) [35 Geo. III. c. 77.] An Act for Improving the Drainage of the Middle and South Levels, Part of the Great Level of the Fens, called Bedford Level and the Low Lands adjoining or near the said Levels; as also the Lands adjoining or near to the River Ouse in the County of Norfolk, draining through the same to sea by the Harbour of King's Lynn in the said County, and for altering and improving the navigation of the said River Ouse, from or near a Place called Eau Brink in the parish of Wiggenhall St. Mary, in the said county, to the said Harbour of King's Lynn; and for improving and preserving the Navigation of the Several Rivers communicating with the said River Ouse. Wisbech and Fenland Museum.

Eau Brink Cut Proprietors. (1793). The Case of Proprietors situate on East side of the River Ouse, through, or near which, the Cut from Eau Brink to Lynn is intended to pass. Norfolk Museums Service

Rennie, John. (1793). To the committee of landowners and others interested in the improvement of the Outfall of the River Ouse. Google Books.

Reports of the Late John Smeaton. Made on Various Occasions, in the course of his employment as a civil engineer. 2nd edition. Vol. 2 M. Taylor (1837). p.135-147.

Sheepshanks, Thomas. (1792). Committee of Landowners and others interested in the Improvement of the Outfall of the River Ouse. British Library English Short Title Collection.

Watté, John & Cubit, Thomas. (1791). For the Better Drainage of the South and Middle Levels of the Fens and other lands bordering upon both sides of the River Ouse and amending the Outfall of the said River by a New Cut or Channel from Eau Brink to Lynn. Wisbech Library C29 Glass Case.

Watté, John & Cubit, Thomas. (1795) A map of the River Ouse from the town of St. Ives to its outfall in King's Lynn Shewing the several navigable Rivers also the proposed New Cut. (that part of the River Ouse from St. Germans to King's Lynn with the line of the intended New Cut. The above line and Dimensions of the Cut is a true reduced Copy of the Plan as Drawn and settled by Sir Thomas Page and Mr. Mylne). Norfolk Record Office.

Yorke, P. Earl of Hardwicke. (1793). Observations Upon the Eau-Brink Cut: With a Proposal Offered to the Consideration of the Friends of the Drainage. Google Books.


**Supporting Resources.**

Ash, Eric H. (2017). The Draining of the Fens; Projectors, Popular Politics and State Building in Early Modern England. Baltimore: John Hopkins University Press.

Barney, John. (2000). The Defence of Norfolk 1793-1815. Norfolk in the Napoleonic Wars. Norwich: Mintaka Books.

Barney, John. (2000). The Trials of Wells Harbour. Mintaka Books, Norwich.

Carmen, W.Y. (1955). Sir Thomas Hyde Page, Engineer. Journal of the Society for Army Historical Research. Vol. 33. p.61-62.

Clarke, James Stanier & McArthur, John. (1809). The Life of Admiral Lord Nelson, K.B. Vol. 1. London: T. Cadell & W. Davies.

Dugdale, Sir William. (1662). The History of Imbanking and Draining of Diverse Fens and Marshes. Revised and Corrected by Charles Nalson Cole. (1772) London: Richard Geast.

Edwards, Eddie. (2017). Ouse or Hundred Foot Washes History and Management Overview. http://www.ousewashes.info/overview. htm

Golan, Tal. (2004). Laws of Men and Laws of Nature: The History of Scientific Expert Testimony in England and America. Massachusetts: Harvard University Press.

Gott, Tony. (2021) North Isles Family History. http://www.bayanne. info/Shetland

Green, John. (2016) Descendants of Hosea Anderson of Aywick. http://www.green.gen.name/hoseason

Hillen, Henry J. (1907). History of the Borough of King's Lynn. Norwich: East of England Newspaper Company.

Hiscocks, Richard. (2018). Sir Andrew Snape Hamond https:// morethannelson.com/officer/sir-andrew-snape-hamond/

Hobhouse, Hermione. (1971). Thomas Cubitt, Master Builder. London: Macmillan.

Hoppit, Julian. (2017). Britain's Political Economies: Parliament and Economic life, 1660-1800. Cambridge: Cambridge University Press.

Howard, Elizabeth. (2015). Downham Riots 1816. A History of Downham Market. https://www.downhammarkethistory. co.uk/2015/09/23/downham-riots-1816/

Howling, Bryan (2008). Terrington St. Clement History Group. http://www. terringtonhistory.co.uk

Kingsley, Nick. (2017). Bagge of Islington Hall, Stradsett Hall and Gaywood Hall. http://landedfamilies.blogspot.com/2017/11/310-bagge-of-islington-hall-stradsett.html

Mackie, Charles. (1901). Norfolk Annals Vol. 1. 1801-1850 http://www.hellenicaworld.com/UK/Literature/CharlesMackie/en/NorfolkAnnals1.html

Marshall, Douglas W. (1980). Military Maps of the Eighteenth-Century and the Tower of London Drawing Room. Imago Mundi, Vol. 32, Lympne, International Society for the History of Cartography. JSTOR, www.jstor.org/stable/1150672 p.21-44.

Mitchell, June & Tilney All Saints Local History Group. (2011). Tilney All Saints in Living Memory. Tilney All Saints.

National Rivers Authority Anglian Region. (1991). King's Lynn Flood Defences, Anglian 70.

Petty, Mike. (2021). Mike Petty's Guide to Websites for Researching Cambridgeshire's history. http://www.mikepetty.org.uk/websites.html

Rickard, J. (2006). Sea Fencibles, 1798-1810. http://www.historyofwar.org/articles/weapons_sea_fencibles.html

Rosselli, John. (1971). An Indian Governor in the Norfolk Marshland: Lord William Bentinck as Improver, 1809-27. The Agricultural History Review Vol. 19, No. 1, p.42-64.

Roth, R. & Beachey, R. (2016). Who Ran the Cities? City Elites and Urban Power Structures in Europe and North America, 1750–1940 (Historical Urban Studies Series) London: Routledge.

Shaw, Chris (Ed.) (2021). Downham Market & Around - Local Parish Histories. https://www.downhammarketparishes.uk/home

Skempton, Alec W. et al. (2002). A Biographical Dictionary of Civil Engineers in Great Britain and Ireland, Vol, 1, London: Thomas Telford. Institution of Civil Engineers (ICE).

Sykes, P. (2002). Borough of King's Lynn 1524-1835: An index of Mayors, Aldermen, Common Councillors, Officials & Some others, (unpublished guide). King's Lynn Archives.

Thomas, Dick. (2010). Thomas Townshend Thomas and his relationship with the Townshend Family. http://afamilyhistory.co.uk/wp-content/uploads/2015/10/TTT-and-the-Townshend1.pdf

Verbruggen, Jan Adrianus. (2005). The Correspondence of Jan Daniel Huichelbos Van Liender with James Watt. Doctoral Thesis, University of Twente, Enshede, Netherlands.

Walker, Thomas James. (1913). The Depot for Prisoners of War at Norman Cross, Huntingdonshire. 1796 to 1816. London, Constable.

Ward, Robert. (2007). The Man Who Buried Nelson: The Surprising Life of Robert Mylne. Stroud, Gloucestershire. Tempus Publishing.

Watson, Garth. (1989). The Smeatonians: London: Thomas Telford. Institution of Civil Engineers (ICE).

Wells, Samuel. (1828). The History of the Drainage of the great Level of the Fens, called Bedford Level; with the constitution and laws of the Bedford Level Corporation. Vol. 1 1828 and Vol. 2 1830. London. Bedford Level Corporation.

# Picture Credits

View of the opening of the Eaubrink Cut, King's Lynn, Norfolk 1821, Artist/maker: Unknown. Courtesy Norfolk Museum Service (Lynn Museum, King's Lynn).

Sir Thomas Hyde Page (1746-1821) holding a Plan of Fort Landguard, Felixstowe, Suffolk. Portrait by James Northcote, RA. Tyntesfield, The Gibbs Collection © National Trust Images

Robert Mylne, (1734-1811) Architect and engineer. Portrait by Henry Adlard after Maria Mylne. © National Galleries of Scotland. Bequeathed by William Finlay Watson, 1886.

John Rennie, (1761-1821) Engineer. Portrait by Sir Henry Raeburn. © National Galleries of Scotland. Purchased 1957 with assistance from the Art Fund (London-Scot Bequest).

Sir Andrew Snape Hamond, Bart., (1738-1828). Portrait by Sir Thomas Lawrence owned by Sir Egerton Hamond Graeme. NH 120879, Courtesy of the Naval History & Heritage Command.

Vice Admiral William Bentinck, (1764-1813), as a Captain in 1787. Portrait by George Romney. © National Maritime Museum, Greenwich, London.

Sir Martin Brown Folkes, Bart. by C. Turner, 1816; engraving on paper by T. Barber: © Norfolk Museum Service (Norwich Castle Museum & Art Gallery).